# PSYCHIATRY

## for

## Pastors, Students and Nurses

# PSYCHIATRY

*for*

## Pastors, Students and Nurses

*by*

## Jacob D. Mulder, S.B., M.D.

Superintendent and Medical Director
of Pinerest Sanitarium and
Christian Psychopathic Hospital,
Grand Rapids, Mich., R. R. 1

Chairman of
Division of Neuro-Psychiatry
of the Staff of Blodgett Memorial Hospital
Grand Rapids, Mich.

Fellow of the
American Medical Association
and the
American Psychiatric Association

WM. B. EERDMANS PUBLISHING COMPANY
Grand Rapids          1954          Michigan

PSYCHIATRY FOR PASTORS, STUDENTS AND NURSES
*by* JACOB D. MULDER, S.B., M.D.

*Copyright*, 1939, *by*
*Wm. B. Eerdmans Publishing Co.*

*Set up and printed, March,* 1939
*Fifth printing, October,* 1954

PRINTED IN THE UNITED STATES OF AMERICA

# Introduction

The author of this book has asked me to write an introduction to his little volume, a request to which I gladly accede, especially too because I am his debtor for the very fine clinic he conducts annually at his hospital for my class in abnormal psychology.

From its very nature this book is limited in its appeal. It is intended neither for Everyman, nor for the specialist in either psychology or psychiatry. As the preface indicates, this book is intended for students, nurses, and the clergy. I wish to commend it especially to the latter. They cannot but profit by studying it carefully.

While the author makes no claim to literary artistry, I can assure the reader that he is in no wise obscure. Nobody at all equipped to profit by the reading of such a book as this will have to guess at the meaning.

Considering its size the book is surprisingly rich in case-material derived from the author's own files. The uninformed reader might see a certain lack of proportion between the brief descriptions of the various psychoses and the generous space given to case-histories. As a matter of fact this is, in my opinion, the outstanding merit of the book. Moreover, some of the cases cited are especially illuminating, notably case 13. I do not at this moment recall a more beautiful illustration of the gradual deterioration of a schizophrenic mind. The attentive reader will learn more about the real nature of schizophrenia from the reading of this one case-history than from twice the pages of description.

There is an old adage to the effect that a little knowledge is a dangerous thing. It is only too true, but the inference ordinarily drawn from it is false. It is false that a little knowledge is bad. A breadknife is patently a dangerous thing, but few would say it is bad. Aristotle would unhesitatingly pronounce it good. Of course, one must know why and how to use it. So a little knowledge, which is all anybody can have about most things of which he knows at all, *is good provided we remember our knowledge is little.*

It is so here. The reader is urged to take to heart the author's warning in the preface. He who carefully reads this book will know a little, a very little about abnormal people, but he is incapable of diagnosing insanity, (except, of course, in those pronounced cases where even a child observes the abnormality), much less is he equipped to state the particular type. I have been amazed and on occasion appalled at the snap diagnoses of some laymen, who tell offhand that So-and-So is a paranoiac or a paretic. One should know that experienced psychiatrists after daily observation of a patient for half a year or longer often hesitate to say whether they have, for example, a case of true paranoia or of the paranoid form of schizophrenia.

However, the knowledge derived from this book, especially if supplemented by further study, may keep a minister, let us say, from the sad error of advocating discipline in a case where compassion really is in place.

J. BROENE

Calvin College,
Grand Rapids, Mich.

# Preface

This book is written primarily for nurses, students and those performing pastoral work, to equip them better in a field rapidly gaining in public interest and attention. Besides academic sources, it has as background the history and daily personal study of 1,800 patients over periods of one month to sixteen years.

The outstanding types of mental disturbance are briefly described from the viewpoints, respectively, of symptoms, course of the disease, treatment, social dangers, and outcome. Of these types the more common are illustrated by "case-histories" in which the patients' own words are used whenever possible.

The final pages contain a discussion of mental disturbance as related to disease, crime and delinquency, suicide, responsibility, demon possession, normal depression, marriage, and religion.

Do not try to reach your own conclusions on the basis of information obtained in this treatise. In any case of what appears to be mental disturbance a qualified psychiatrist should always be consulted. The field of psychiatry is large, obscure, and full of difficult problems, even to the specialist.

Acknowledgment is gratefully made for aid, advice, and criticism received in the preparation of this book.

JACOB D. MULDER

# Contents

# CHAPTER I

# Causes of Mental Disturbance

IN CONSIDERING the cause of mental disturb- *Two* ance, there are two important factors to be noted. *factors in* The first is the physical sub-structure, and the second *Mental* the emotional and psychic component. *disturbance*

The first concerns the brain and all other bodily *I. Brain +* structures necessary for mental functioning. A poorly *bodily* developed, or partially destroyed or diseased brain, makes normal mental activity impossible. The same holds true when internal secretory glands are missing or impaired. A child in whom at birth certain of these *glands* glands are absent, is not only physically but also mentally abnormal. But so, too, changes in the activity of these glands, upsetting their inter-related balance, lead to mental and emotional instability. Such changes *puberty* probably account for the many cases of mental disturb- ance found at puberty (13 to 18), or at the climacteric *climacteric* (change of life 45 to 55). It is during these two spans, respectively, that the sex glands, which belong to the *Sex* internal secretory class, begin and end their specific *glands* functions.

A very important cause of mental disturbance of all types is therefore to be found in abnormal physical conditions, originating in defective bodily develop-

13

ment or due to destructive factors occurring during the life of the organism. Mental disturbance is, however, found only where we have that intricate mysterious union of Soma and Psyche, body and soul. Insanity in the strict sense of the word is not found in the animal kingdom. There must be a certain amount of mental development to have a true psychosis. It is rarely found in children below thirteen. Some emotional stability and intellectual maturity are evidently essential before insanity can make its appearance. In other words, "It demands a certain amount of intelligence to become insane," as a certain author expressed it.

*No insanity in animals*

The origin of the functional psychoses, I believe, is probably as follows: The mind has its problems for which it tries to find a solution; unsuccessful, it stirs up an emotional reaction of greater intensity than the physical structure or soma can bear, and the result is a dissociation or blocking, either complete or partial, in the amazingly intricate nervous structure. In the milder forms no permanent destruction results; slowly normal relations are re-established. But in the more severe forms, a vicious circle is evidently created, ever aggravating the injury to the soma or physical substratum.

*origin of functional psychosis*

The cause of mental disturbance may therefore in its primary aspect be either functional or organic, but in its final result probably always has an additional organic or bodily factor as its basis.

?

As far as the hereditary causes are concerned, this brings up a complicated problem. On the one hand it is true that there often is a hereditary causation. We

*Hereditary*

at times find many cases of mental disturbance in one family. But on the other hand, there is scarcely a family that has not one or more mentally disturbed in its family tree. Mental disturbance is a much more common occurrence than we care to admit. One out of every eighteen persons at some time needs institutional care. I do feel convinced that a predisposition toward mental disturbance is in most of our functional cases present at birth. This congenital characteristic is not necessarily inherent in the chromosome of the parent cells, but may have its origin during the embryonic or foetal life. As the embryo develops from a single cell to billions and slowly assumes form, many qualities may became warped due to disease in the organism. Minor abnormalities in the newborn may then, as the child develops, present themselves as serious disease entities in later life, especially during periods of stress and strain.

Focusing our attention upon these multiple possibilities of congenital defect or disturbance, we might well reach the conclusion that the average man's reserve is small and that we all walk on a precipice. The opposite, however, is true. Fact is that God has supplied every organ of the average human body with an immense over-efficiency far beyond its needs, which also holds true for the structure through which the human mind operates. This accounts for the fact that notwithstanding the immense stress and strain to which mankind is subjected during times of war, pestilence, famine, and depression, the increase in mental derangement is slight. There are those among us, however, in

*Some have small surplus.*

whom the surplus of efficiency is small; — the oil, as it were, soon burns out. In a rural society, as most people lived some fifty years ago, these individuals often succeeded in the struggle for existence, but the present age of speed and competition far exceeds their endurance.

## Causes of Mental Disturbance

More than one of the following factors are often causative in the production of mental disease:

1. Heredity or hereditary tendencies.
2. Congenital defects. *may come during embryonic or foetal life.*
3. Psychogenic and emotional causes.
4. Predisposing life periods: puberty, childbirth, involution. *Decline or opposite to evolution. Change of*
5. Poisons: alcohol, opium (morphine, heroin), cocaine, bromides, lead, marihuana (cannibas sativa or hemp).
6. Infections: pneumonia, typhoid, meningitis, encephalitis, focal infections, etc.
7. Exhaustion.
8. Injuries of the head and brain tumors.
9. Bodily diseases: pellagra, diabetes, pernicious anemia, heart and kidney disease.
10. Endocrine, chemical or metabolic disturbance.
11. Syphilis.
12. Arteriosclerosis.
13. Senility. *Old Age*

## Classification of Mental Diseases

*Official Classification as Adopted and Amended by The American Psychiatric Association.*

1. Manic-depressive psychoses
   a. Manic type
   b. Depressive type
   c. Other types
2. Involution melancholia
3. Dementia praecox (schizophrenia)
   Simple type
   Hebephrenic
   Katatonic
   Paranoid
4. Paranoia and paranoid conditions
5. Epileptic psychoses
6. Psychoneuroses and neuroses
   a. Hysterical type
   b. Psychasthenic type (anxiety and obsessive forms)
   c. Neurasthenic type
   d. Other types
7. Psychoses with psychopathic personality
8. Psychoses with mental deficiency
9. Traumatic psychoses
10. Senile psychoses
11. Psychoses with cerebral arteriosclerosis
12. General paralysis
13. Psychoses with cerebral syphilis
14. Psychoses with Huntington's chorea
15. Psychoses with brain tumor
16. Psychoses with other brain or nervous diseases
    a. Encephalitis lethargica (sleeping sickness)
    b. Acute chorea
    c. Tabes dorsalis

d. Multiple sclerosis
e. Meningitis, tubercular or other forms
f. Paralysis agitans
g. Cerebral embolism

17. Alcoholic psychoses
a. Delirium tremens
b. Korsakow's psychosis
c. Acute hallucinosis
d. Other types, acute or chronic

18. Psychoses due to drugs and other exogenous toxins
a. Opium, (morphine, heroin, codein), cocaine, bromides, chloral
b. Metals, as lead, arsenic, etc.
c. Gases
d. Other exogenous toxins

19. Psychoses with pellagra

20. Psychoses with other somatic diseases
a. Delirium with infectious diseases
b. Post-infectious psychosis
c. Exhaustion delirium
d. Delirium of unknown origin
e. Cardio-renal diseases
f. Diseases of the ductless glands
g. Other diseases or conditions

21. Undiagnosed psychoses

22. Without psychosis
a. Epilepsy without psychosis
b. Alcoholism without psychosis
c. Drug addiction without psychosis
d. Psychopathic personality without psychosis
e. Mental deficiency without psychosis
f. Other conditions

*Manic: extreme and impulsive or uncontrollable energy.*

# CHAPTER II

# Manic-Depressive Psychoses

THIS disease runs its course in waves or phases. The crest of the wave represents a period of excitement and well-being; the trough a condition of inhibition and gloom. The number of waves that occur during a life time may be many or few; the duration of each wave, days or decades. It is a disease of relatively frequent occurrence, some 35% of admissions belong to this group. Besides these two outstanding phases there are mixed conditions. In cases designated as agitated depression, there is depression of the emotions, but increased physical activity and flight of ideas; and in its opposite, maniacal stupor, the emotions show exaltation, while thinking and action are inhibited.

*Runs in waves of 2 phases*

*Mixed Conditions*

In contradistinction from the schizoid condition, which usually occurs in the shut-in types of personality, this disease is largely linked to the sociable, extravert type.

*autistic*

*wishful thinking*

## A. HYPOMANIA (or mild mania)

This group, if recovery is early, are often not recognized.

If a law-abiding, calm, and well-behaved individual has periods during which he becomes bold, breezy, ag-

gressive, unreliable, insulting, it is well to remember
the possibility that he is suffering from a mild attack
of mania.

## B. MANIC PHASE.

Symptoms

*Symptoms:* The first symptom noticed may be a
marked personality change. The subject becomes loud,
profane, abusive. An amazing self-confidence drives
him into false business ventures and foolish undertak-
ings. He dresses gaily and decorates himself foolishly.
There is pressure of activity which robs him of sleep,
food and rest; and pressure of speech resulting in a
flight of ideas often evident in senseless rhyming. Finally, coherence is lost completely and confusion results.
He misidentifies people around him and becomes disoriented as to time, place, and person.

Hallucinations, although often present, are not outstanding.

delusions

The delusions from which he suffers are exaggerated
and may be persecutory. Recovery leads to perfect
readjustment in the community. There is no deterioration.

Danger

Danger to self, home, and society at times is marked,
mainly because the patient is so extremely impulsive.
The sufferer is usually soon placed in confinement, however, as he inspires fear in home and environment.

## C. THE DEPRESSED PHASE.

This condition often precedes or follows a manic
attack. The depression may be mild or fleeting, or
serious and chronic.

Coherence: logical Thinking

hypochondria: Morbid concern about ones health with exaggeration of every trifling symptom.

MANIC-DEPRESSIVE PSYCHOSES          21

*Symptoms*: There is present a fear of impending Symptoms misfortune or anxiety, a cause for which cannot be found. The disease may from this point develop in two directions. In many patients activity becomes decreased and thought retarded; this group finally may become mute and sink into deep stupor. In a smaller number the anxiety results in a pressure of activity and thought; these patients often rapidly walk the floor wringing their hands and muttering condemnatory phrases about self or repeating some expression of dreadful calamity (Agitated depression).

Hallucinations, if present, are usually terrifying. De- Hallucinations lusions of unworthiness, hopelessness, and self-accusa- Delusions tion are common. They have committed the unpardonable sin and are the personification of evil. Suspicion against persons of the household, especially the mate, are frequent. Perversion of taste and smell often result in ideas of poisoning. Food and drink are for this reason refused and artificial feeding must be resorted to. Most depressed also suffer from hypochon- hypochondriacal delusions. ("A morbid concern about the dria. health and exaggerated attention to any unusual bodily or mental sensation.") They imagine that their brain, stomach, or bladder is being slowly eaten away or has stopped functioning. The heart especially gives immense concern.

The danger of suicide is great; of homicide common. Danger They frequently converse normally in the presence of strangers. The public or those not of the household for this reason often do not realize danger until some act of violence has been committed.

*Strang fact*

This form of mental disturbance well illustrates the fact that insanity often creates no minus but a plus in the human mind. Many acute and not a few chronic mental patients are more sensitive to impressions and more rapid in sizing up a situation than the normal. There is no loss of mental content or functions, but a delusion is added which warps the personality misguiding judgment and obscuring faith. "The insane person has not actually lost some part of his soul, for example, his intelligence, reason or will." (Bavinck, H., *Verzamelde Opstellen,* Amsterdam, 1921, p. 201).

*Quote*

*Recovery*

Recovery usually takes place in from 2 months to 2 years.

In about 50% of patients who suffer from this condition, there is one attack, and no recurrence.

*Therapy*

*Suggestions as to psychotherapy:*

Never suggest to a depressed patient that he must snap out of it. This is cruel. The depressed patient is a helpless sufferer. These patients need protection and must be daily encouraged and urged to struggle through the maelstrom in which they are engulfed.

The darkness that surrounds them is often absolute, and no ray of light can penetrate this night until the depression (a disease entity) subsides.

HYPOMANIA (Case 1)
(a) Periodic attacks of excitement.
(b) Complete recovery between attacks.
(c) Demonstrates necessity of early institutionalization.

Patient was bright, good-natured, sociable and ambitious. She cared little for the opposite sex until a few weeks before admission.

Physically, she had for years complained much of palpitation of the heart, gastro-intestinal upsets, and for the last year had fainting spells.

About six weeks before admission this quiet, sickly, self-centered girl suddenly presented another picture. She became talkative, restless, euphoric, irritable, and careless. Her reserved attitude towards the opposite sex changed to a marked, erotic, aggressive reaction.

She ran from home, stole money, falsified checks, rented rooms in hotels, and invited guests. She was apprehended by police for disorderly conduct and later returned home. She promised to reform, but for a second time escaped from the house and went to a distant city.

After entering our hospital, she was very talkative. She told of escapades and seemed proud of all the evil she had done. Her stories were adorned with impossible tales. Truth evidently meant nothing to her and all moral sense was submerged. If asked to be quiet she would become irritable and threaten the nurses. Her appetite was enormous; her sleep disturbed. She roamed from room to room, upsetting this, interfering there. "Just a perfect nuisance," as one of the patients described her.

These periods of well-being and elation were followed by hours of deep gloom. She would then throw herself on the bed and cry as if heartbroken. She said, "I would rather die than be crazy and a good-for-nothing. Let me commit suicide as nobody loves me."

Cases of acute hypomania like the above, should be institutionalized immediately. No girl or boy is more liable to fall into the hands of unscrupulous individuals, than these. They have no inhibition, suffer often from an erotic, sexual urge that can only be controlled by confinement, and should be treated by hydrotherapy as given in mental hospitals.

MANIC-DEPRESSED (Recurrent mania) (Case 2)
(a) Mild attacks of hypomania succeeded by two of major-mania.

(b) Two periods of hospitalization, lasting respectively 3 and 10 years.

(c) Outcome: Of early attacks, complete recovery. Of last attack, poor social adjustment.

*Personal history:*

He was an active, willing and efficient worker, rather high-strung and impulsive, but sociable and pleasant. The early attacks, which lasted a few days, were heralded by restlessness, and irritability. If the condition lasted more than a few weeks, he began to spend money foolishly, wrote checks beyond deposits; bought, paid for, and forgot to take purchased article home.

These minor attacks which caused the family much grief, finally resulted in a major attack lasting 3 years. During this attack he developed an amazing feeling of well-being. He would exclaim, "I am a marvel to be wondered at, as I can accomplish anything and do everything." To save time on his way home from the shop, he would hail taxis and leave his own car in town. Instead of minor irregularities in spending, he made attempts to buy carload lots. If reprimanded, he would fly into a fury and threaten to do bodily harm.

In that condition he was committed to the hospital. There he became still more disturbed, assaultive, noisy, and destructive. These periods of violence were associated with a paranoid content. He was convinced that the state, society, and the church were all plotting against him. He accused Doctor and nurses of malicious intent. Wrote letters to state and church officials in order to obtain freedom and bring punishment upon us who detained him. His days were spent in irritating nurses and patients. By looks, gestures, insinuations, etc., he would keep things in turmoil and make work extremely unpleasant for a conscientious nurse. In the still hours of the night, when he well knew that nurses desired to have quiet, he would take fiendish delight in bursting forth with thundering voice into song or cursing. His voice was then of such volume that it could be heard far and wide through the quiet night.

The only method of control was the continuous bath, but even that was not always effective. At times it seemed as if nothing could inhibit the immense pressure under which he labored. During such periods of excitement the sweat could be wrung from his garments, and would drop from his chin and tips of his fingers.

Result: Recovery with good social adjustment.

He wrote me the following letter after recovery had taken place: "Kindly fill out my release papers at the probate court in order that I may be a free man and can again enjoy my privileges as a citizen."

Cases in which excitement is of as long a duration and in whom there is such fiendish delight in causing disturbance, are rare. Short periods of these conditions are, however, common.

As their logic is perfect, their writing and conversational talent amazing, they may give hospital authorities concern by publishing far and wide their perverted impression in regard to treatment received.

After complete recovery, the manic patients are the most appreciative that leave our hospital. If they are critical after discharge, it usually indicates that recovery was partial and not complete.

It is often with apprehension that we see these patients resume their places in society, as mania is frequently followed by short periods of depression, a mental state almost invariably containing suicidal content.

### DEPRESSION (Case 3)

(a) *Outstanding symptoms*: Ideas of unworthiness, self-accusation, hopelessness, apprehension, irritability and suicidal content.

(b) *Outcome*: Complete recovery.

*Extracts* from *letters* written by *patient*:

"You have received letters and cards from my husband saying I had to go here to rest from shocked nerves. It is true my nerves were all upset, but it was the result of a great sin I committed. Therefore God brought this upon me and my family. [The sin consisted in advising her husband to borrow money.] From that day I lost all interest in spiritual things. The Spirit left me. I cannot pray or read and I have no rest. I have ruined my family. I began to get so nervous at home I could not sleep or sit still. It was an evil disease God put upon me for my sin. I am not sick in body. It is all my sin. I do not know what the end will be. All my spiritual life is gone. I have wilfully sinned and God left me. I suffer. You cannot understand how much. Healthy in body and mind with this awful thing in my soul and no hope for the end. I have ruined myself and my family. Horrible thoughts are constantly going through my mind."

Report of relatives: This condition had been coming on for some years. The early symptoms had been suspiciousness and extreme irritability toward husband and near relatives. Frequently she talked all night long, keeping everyone in a state of tension. A common expression was the outcry of "Sin, Sin, all Sin. My soul is lost. I hate the light." [This would be accompanied by motions of her hands as if trying to hide from the light.] At times she became aggressive and attacked members of the family or attempted self-destruction by dashing herself on the floor . . . In the presence of strangers she was usually composed!

In the hospital she was able to control her impulsive, delusional thoughts. At various times, however, she went into spells during which she somersaulted, screamed, and shivered. She ascribed these to visions of horrible apparitions. She longed for a way of escape (suicide) and would request the nurses for assistance to obtain this goal.

"I know," she said, "the nurses think I am queer because I walk all the time. [restlessness] I hear them speak about it to each other. [Ideas of reference. She believed all conversation of nurses concerned her.] When I had been here six weeks, a thought came to the Doctor, from Satan, that I could go home for a day. [This was a suggestion that she had herself made to her husband and relatives. The intention was to obtain an opportunity to commit suicide.] I eat and drink and rest little because I have to walk from morning till night. No rest for me. I will live on this way till the end of time. [This is a very common delusion in the depressed. It pictures an endless, reckless, continuous *present*.] Other patients have asked me for what reason I am here and what I worry about. [She believes others consider her normal.] I never answer. This is only the beginning of my suffering. I am not insane but I have learned since I am here that most of them [the patients] say they are not insane. Never has such a terrible thing happened before." (She considers herself especially ordained to suffer and be thus punished. An exaggerated delusion of self-importance.)

This patient after some five years of suffering recovered completely and now for years has lived a well-adjusted life in home, society, and church.

(Case 4)

The symptoms of depression in this case are interpreted by the patient mainly in terms of religious values. To demonstrate that there is great variance in the interpretation placed on symptoms of depression by the patients themselves, I am adding cases 4 (a) and 4 (b).

*Report from Pastor*:

She has been too serious in regard to spiritual matters. From the time she made confession of faith she has assumed a far too spiritual aspect of obtaining the heights of sanctification. Being discouraged, she went to the other extreme, stating that every blessing in this world will be a testimony against her and consequently the sooner she would end it all the better. As a catechumen, she was to be counted with the very best. She has always shown great interest in spiritual matters; fact is, sometimes too much for a young girl.

*Patient's own report of herself*:

"I could learn well but was always afraid I would fail. If my work was below 90 I was not satisfied. If the teacher scolded, it always seemed for me [Hypersensitive and over-conscientious].

"I lost interest in everything. I feel this way — the devil has me anyway [hopeless]. I am just lying waiting for the end. I see all the sin I do, but there is no forgiveness. Thousands of people get lost, but they care; dition. About 4 years ago I began to realize that there was something wrong with me."

"Yes, I realize very well that I do much greater wrong sitting here than working hard at home, and yet I know very well I don't deserve a place in that home any more. Don't feel sorry for me, and I seek not one bit of sympathy. I have made life miserable for the *whole* communi- I do not. As long as I have been able to realize what religion was I have been worried about my spiritual con- ty, [notice the exaggeration of her estimation of self] and left things in an awful mess, not appreciating what good everybody tried to do for me. A true type of Lot's wife, seeking to save myself. I'm lost and have made so many promises which I failed to keep. Feel assured that you are free of my blood. I am spiritually dead. Don't feel sorry for me. I think about you all but I should be erased from your minds."

Nurses reported that patient hears voices urging her to commit suicide. She is often frantic, paces halls, hitting self, wringing hands, calling, "Oh, I'm lost."

She often seems in agony. She speaks of faces peering into hers, which take the form of shadows. She also sees animals but cannot tell what they are, for they appear as shadows. She shudders as she tells these things, expressing horror of them.

## (Case 4 a)

The interpretation of the depressed feelings in this patient has a moral significance. This case shows, in addition to moral perversions, an extreme degree of hatefulness toward those she formerly loved.

"It would have been better," she said, "if I were dead. I never thought I would turn out to be such a mother, but it seems I am helpless. I was extremely cranky last summer before I changed. I don't know what to make of things. How can I be so hardhearted as to leave my family? I don't see how I could have fallen so low. There is no more love in my heart. I created a dreadful hatred for you which cannot change. God doesn't seem to mean anything to me, and although I don't exhibit any hatred, it is in me. I would delight in being in hell. I am filled with hatred and swearing. I just hate my husband and children. It makes me tremble with anger when I think of them. I don't care what I do. An evil power is talking to me. My heart seems to turn inside out when I think of home.

"I know I was different once. My nature is changed. Eight years ago when I was this way I wanted to rob banks to get my name in the paper. I associated with people of ill fame. I desired to be in a den of thieves or a robber's wife. Now I want to marry a cast-out and forsake my husband and children.

"I would a million times sooner suffer any physical pain than to be tormented by the lewd and hateful thoughts that rush through my mind from morn till night."

### (Case 4 b)

The following case, although evidencing religious despair and hateful inclinations, is obsessed mainly with ideas of bodily change.

"I want an X-Ray taken of my head to prove that the brain is gone. I am rotting away. God sees the whole of my body and knows all. I am not resting and I am not nervous, but only suffering for sin in a strange way. No thoughts, no bodily pain, just different and feelingless. If I close my eyes in daylight or at night, I do not know the difference. Life is done and ended. I do not see, smell, taste, hear or feel. My whole body is just like stone. I must suffer and let the Lord have His own way. All I can do is ask forgiveness. I can never get better. This is impossible. No man on earth can heal me. I have to wait until the Lord takes me away. I have hope the Lord may forgive me on that last day. How long will that be? I must live on this way till the end of time."

### DEPRESSED, WITH PARANOID CONTENT (Case 5)

(a) *Hospital stay*: 3 months

(b) *Duration* of Psychosis: 1½ years

(c) *Outcome*: Social recovery

The patient whose history I desire to relate, was sociable and good-natured, but somewhat shy and sensitive. Physically she had always enjoyed good health until the age of twenty, but since that date suffered considerably from bodily ills. Mentally she was, however, above all suspicion, until about a year before she came under our care. About that time the death of a member of the family to whom she was greatly attached affected her deeply. Shortly after the funeral, the relatives reported that she had become shut-in, depressed, and morbid.

She arrived home one evening with the story of having been molested by a stranger while shopping. From that date, she repeatedly spoke of having been terrorized by that same individual. Her husband at this time did not at all appreciate that this spelled something serious. Even when she began to tell him of accusatory voices that troubled her daily, he did not realize that her mind had become sick and that she therefore was in need of protection.

Fact was that she was seeing imaginary persons and was hearing voices that did not originate in space. In other words, she was at times strongly hallucinated. Her own self-accusing thoughts were assuming form. Objects of vision and sound, as real as her senses had ever received, were being created in her own mind and projected into space. These voices not only accused her of crimes and proclaimed her a worthless wretch, but urged her as Job's wife did Job, "Curse God and die!"

After some four weeks, during which the suffering became even more intense, the delusional self concocted a plan of self-destruction, a plan that would destroy her, wipe out their mortgaged home and thus release her husband of all the wretchedness she had caused him. To hide the crime, she wrote unsigned threatening letters to herself. But the suicide attempt failed. In the agony of near-death she managed to tear loose not only from her delusions, but also from self-applied physical bonds.

Because of the weird tale, to which she held for nine days, (namely, that a man was the perpetrator) she was remanded to jail. During these nine days she suffered intensely, but slowly on reality again assumed form, and the delusional picture cleared up. In this depressed self-accusatory mental state, she readily admitted to the sheriff that she had performed the deed and that criminal intent was the outstanding motive.

The prosecuting attorney charged that the respondent had wilfully, unlawfully and maliciously committed the crime.

Three physicians (not psychiatrists) testified that in their opinion the respondent on the date said offense was committed was insane, and the victim of irresistible impulse, compelling her to commit deeds by her known to be wrong, and that her ability to distinguish between right and wrong was impaired.

The judge sent her to our hospital.

For some months I daily watched this mild-mannered, delicate, quiet, mentally clear but mildly hallucinated patient. Unwavering was her story of the dreadful figure and voices, that spurred her on to plan and commit the dreadful act.

*Her story*:

"For the past year I noticed ringing and blowing in my ears, [early hallucinatory phenomena] and for the last four months voices frequently spoke to me. This made me fearful. It drew me from my religion. I just had the feeling as if I was held by someone. I planned to kill myself for four weeks before I tried it. I was driven all this time. Voices kept saying, 'Why should you have all this trouble if God is true?' I saw that figure constantly, especially the last day. It was terrible. I was fighting with the figure. He was tall and awfully red. His hands did not seem human. Three or four weeks before my attempt at suicide he was in the house too. The method I followed was suggested to me lately. After the attempt, I can't tell you what a relief I have had. No words can express it."

*This case demonstrates:*

1. That an apparently normal individual may, nevertheless, be a sufferer from a serious mental condition.

2. The presence of positively abnormal mental symptoms, even though few, makes it necessary to judge and treat such a person as sick and not as a criminal.

3. Only such a procedure does justice to and can protect both individual and society. Cases like the above should remain under observation as long as they live and never fill positions of responsibility.

## DEPRESSION (Case 6)

This patient was a middle-aged male. He had ten years before admission suffered from a similar attack.

Outcome of both attacks: Complete recovery.

Past history: He was bright, good-natured, sociable, ambitious, persevering, and religiously inclined.

The onset of the depression was very gradual and began with sleeplessness, restlessness, and forebodings of impending calamity. The first serious symptom originated about a year after the onset. He told his wife at this time that people were watching him and that his home and other possessions would be taken from him.

One evening returning home from work the depression drove him to attempt suicide by walking in front of an interurban train. He was, however, noticed and taken home. That night he made four other attempts at self-destruction but failed to reach his goal. (After one attempt at suicide is made an early repetition is extremely frequent).

Patient's own history as given on the date of admission:

"About a year ago I became troubled with sleeplessness. I would wake up at 2 or 3 A.M. and could not get back to sleep. My dreams were terrifying. I would dream of floods and narrow escapes. After awakening I suffered agony. I was restless and though inhibited in my movements often walked the floor till morning. Work gave some relief, but former pleasures, as traveling, social contacts, etc., would aggravate my suffering. In the evening I felt most at ease. At times, after the lights were lit, the anxiety seemed completely gone. [This is a very common occurrence among the depressed.]

"I suffered much of pressure within my head, dizziness, gastric distress, and a buzzing in my ears, resembling the sound of crickets or bells. I also noticed voices calling me by name, accusing me of doing evil and suggesting self-destruction. Last week I attempted suicide by walking on the car tracks. Since that time I have repeatedly planned to end it. I said to my wife, 'I can't any longer. My mind can't stand it.' "

The first few months after admission to our hospital his condition became gradually worse. The agitated depression changed to stupor, moaning to silence and fear to confusion. In this condition he was placed in bed and remained there motionless for several months. During much of this period he had to be fed and cared for as a child. The depression then very slowly cleared up and both mental and physical activities returned to normal.

He returned home recovered and resumed his former position in the home, society, and church.

# CHAPTER III

## Involution Melancholia

THIS disease is, according to many authorities, close-ly allied to the manic-depressive psychosis. The difference in symptomatology probably results from the influence upon the organism of somatic, chemical, and emotional changes found at the change of life period.

It makes its appearance a little later in the life of the male than in the female. In women, the age of its occurrence is usually between 40 and 50; in men between 50 and 60.

The outstanding early symptoms are anxiety, inde-cision, apprehension, disturbed sleep and appetite, and the appearance in the sensorium of strange sensa-tions from every bodily organ. Most of these cases have the following in common: a feeling of hopelessness for time and eternity, and bodily delusions that often cen-ter about urogenital organs and gastro-intestinal tract. A close questioning of these patients also reveals that the sufferer is taking a moral and spiritual inventory of his past life and considers it seriously wanting.

Danger to self, home, and society is at times great. Suicidal tendencies are strong and homicidal attacks may occur. Consciousness usually remains clear, and the sensorium is very alert, which, as in the simple depressions, makes recognition of the disease difficult.

Recovery of mild cases is almost the rule; of more severe cases about 40%.

Deterioration may set in on the basis of arteriosclerosis or early senility.

### Involution Melancholia (Case 7)

(a) Patient had always been well both physically and mentally.

(b) *Irregularity* of menstruation began 2 years before admission.

(c) *Duration* of disease 3 years.

(d) *Outstanding symptoms*: Depression, negativism, irritability, suicidal content, and delusions in connection with intestinal tract and genito-urinary organs.

> About a year before admission, husband made an innocent remark which greatly irritated patient and precipitated the severe symptoms.
>
> From this date patient became rapidly worse and began to express suicidal tendencies. She moaned practically all day long, saying, "I can't get well." She believed she had committed a sin against the Holy Ghost. Her suicidal attempts were many and varied. She tried to run before passing cars, cut her throat with a razor blade, ran away from home and was found near a lake ready to end her miserable existence. She often said, "I wish there was no hereafter." She refused food and became angry if urged to eat. While formerly she had been extremely particular about her dress and home, she now became in-

different and even filthy. Company she shunned and she would try to hide when visitors came. For her children she seemed to have no love or regard, and their pleading urging her to do differently, fell on deaf ears.

Her physical symptoms were also characteristic. After lying awake home for almost a week, a mysterious sensation she said overpowered her in the region of the stomach. From out of the stomach, she said, came a blowing sound. This she believed had caused her stomach to go all to pieces. The food, she said, no longer digests but turns into gas and as such, passes through the bowels.

After a year of suffering in the hospital, the symptoms slowly cleared up. She regained full insight and went home recovered.

Her confession after recovery was that she had been well aware of all that happened during the delusional period, but had simply been unable to resist the contra-social acts. The whole period loomed up before her now as a bad, hideous dream. The fact that she had been ill troubled her little, and she experienced no inferiority feeling when meeting former friends.

## AGITATED DEPRESSION  (Case 8)

This patient could not sleep, walked the floor wringing her hands for hours, made attempts at self-mutilation and threatened suicide.

Her depressed delusions always centered about her home which, at the advice of an architect, she had remodeled. Her contention was that if she had only not caused this home to be remodeled she would have been saved from this affliction.

*Letter written by this patient to her pastor*: (Although brought up in a religious home, she had failed to attend religious services for years, and seemed entirely uninterested in religion until the onset of the depression.)

"Please come to visit me at the Hospital. I want to tell you something to save other souls, if mine is lost." *Letter written by Pastor to patient*: (The Reverend A. had visited her at various times. The letter is therefore a mirror of the patient's mental content as observed by her Pastor.)

"Mrs. X,

"Cutlerville, Mich.

"Dear Friend:

"It was a great surprise to me to read in your letter that you thought your soul was lost. I cannot understand what would make you or anyone think that, since we know that Almighty God is the God of mercy rather than the God of justice. We know that His mercy is above all His works and we also know that He has never denied mercy to anyone. You no doubt recall several examples during the lifetime of our Lord where He showed infinite mercy to mankind. Remember He forgave St. Peter after Peter denied Him. He forgave Mary Magdalene because she loved much. Even the good thief on the cross was forgiven by our Lord because the good thief acknowledged Christ as his Redeemer. That same mercy is still the policy of Christ and of Christ's Church. It was never known and it will never be that Christ or His Church ever denied mercy to anyone who asked for mercy. There is one thing that I want you to do and that is pray to our Lord to restore you to health and then once your nerves are quieted down you will be able to show our Lord that you are very grateful to Him for being so kind to you. Be sure to tell Him that you also want to share in the great mercy He showed for you especially by His death on the cross and your request will be granted.

"Next week is Holy Week, a very fitting time to ask God to have a share in His mercy and you can rest assured that if you ask for mercy it will not be denied you any more than it was denied to Peter or the good thief. I shall also remember you in my prayers and ask God to restore your health and extend His mercy to you that some day you may be happy with Him in Heaven. May God bless you generously.

Sincerely yours in Christ,

Rev. ..............................."

*Outcome*: Complete recovery.

## CHAPTER IV

# Paranoia and Paranoid Conditions

KRAEPELIN (*Paranoia*, p. 212) defines his conception of paranoia as follows: "The insidious development of a permanent and unshakable delusional system, resulting from internal causes, which is accompanied by perfect preservation of clear and orderly thinking, willing, and acting. At the same time a deep-reaching transformation of the whole view of life is usually accomplished."

These are the mental cases who write innumerable letters to church and governmental authorities. There is scarcely a community that does not harbor cases of this type.

True cases are few, but symptoms of this malady are found in many other forms of mental disturbance.

Although true hallucinations are rare, visions are common. They receive orders from God. Satan reveals himself to them and in a nightly attack has attempted to destroy them. In the name of Jehovah who speaks through them they command the hospital force to obey their orders. Delusions of reference are often early symptoms of this dreadful disease. Glances of a passerby, a movement of the hand, a shrug of the shoulder, have a mysterious meaning. They suffer from delusions of grandeur, they have great talents; of family connection, they are of royal birth; of persecution, they are laughed at; slandered, sermons are aimed at them, newspapers write about them under assumed names; of jealousy, their mates are not true to them; of religious grandeur, they are the chosen of God and have supernatural power; of erotic content, they think persons of high estate wish to marry them and are making improper advances. Preachers purposely choose certain texts and have them only in mind when they preach, etc.

The outstanding characteristic of the delusions is that they are systematized. A web is slowly woven by the patient, made up of ideas of reference, false memories, and purely visionary material. The conviction thus obtained is unshakable and permanent.

Dangers to society, self, or home, are not great. They usually manage to remain within the law. If not detected, recognized, and judged as mentally irresponsible, they may cause endless trouble in church and state.

Recovery of true cases probably never occurs.

PARANOIA (Case 9)

(a)  Duration of disease: 20 years.

(b)  Outcome:

　　　1. No deterioration.
　　　2. No signs of recovery.

Before commitment he was an irregular worker and considered lazy. At home he assumed a threatening attitude toward wife and children, destroyed property, including valuable papers.

This man wrote a well-constructed, logical, fatherly letter to his family:

"Dear Wife and children:

"This morning my attention was drawn to the goodness of the Lord shown forth so beautifully in nature. He surely is faithful to His promises made to His servant Noah, the preacher of righteousness. His serene blue sky and the brightness of the Sun which is still that 'strong man, who rejoices to run the race' are evident tokens that He is not yet tired of doing well to mankind. Surely His greatness and His goodness is revealed in the realm of nature. Observing these facts with a grateful heart they should constrain us to honour and glorify Him and with exultant praise give utterance to our gratefulness.

"Our youngest child you certainly do not want to forget. I often look at her sweet little face on the picture I received. I hope you may all grow up in the fear and in the admonition of the Lord, who has all things in the hollow of His hand.

"Best regards to all who may inquire concerning my person, and commended to the loving care of our Heavenly Father, I remain,

"Your loving Husband and Father."

Patient gives the following history of himself:
"I have had a visitation of the third person when I was a child of three and of seven, and after I was married seven years, it came again. This time, during the night, I awoke and thought that someone was walking upstairs. I heard the door open. This door would not make any noise unless someone opened it. I went up-

stairs but no one was there. I went downstairs and was
visited again. I fell on my knees and prayed. Last March
I had a visitation of the second person. He came to me
personally and if he had not appeared personally I
would not be able to be the Saint I am.

"Of late they have been working in my body at night.
I have blue spots on my body in the morning, and great
pain in my neck. My feet at times feel as if they were
broken." (Mistreatment at night by unseen enemies
during sleep is a very common delusion in the paranoid patient.)

Hospital history:

Each day this patient in heathen fashion puts his
hands up, turns to the east, bows three times to the
rising sun and then prays. He shows no interest in work,
never speaks to anyone, never reads, not even the letters
from home. Yet he is well aware of his environment,
well-oriented, eats and sleeps well, and causes no difficulties in the hospital environment.

## PARANOIA (Case 10)

(a) *Hospital stay:*4 years.

(b) *Reason for commitment*: Assault on imagined
persecutors.

(c) *Outcome*: No change in delusional content, but
good social adjustment.

*Patient's History:*

"I have always been persecuted; already for 30 years.
I never was as other people. As a child I always was
alone; also when a student.

"For years they have come in my house at night to spy
on me. My wife refused to believe it, but it is true. When
I wrote articles for a paper, the person whom I assaulted

would have his wife ask my wife to investigate these writings.

"I believe in direct answers to prayer (with the laying on of hands) and have held lectures on this subject. I printed notices of these lectures, but the boys I hired to distribute them would hide or destroy them. For this reason I never had an audience.

"God has revealed himself repeatedly to me. He told me repeatedly that I must leave this place [the hospital] but human mortals detain me here. Before I made the assault, I had received these revelations as to what I had to carry out, and how I was to proceed. God still reveals himself to me each night. He shows me beautiful visions. But it will not do for me to speak about these to mortal men. They are too sacred to be told.

"If I was a murderer, the prophets of old also were murderers when they carried out God's commands [He in his own estimation is a prophet]. But I do not belong in an institution as this, as I have always lived a pure life [perfectionism]. I should not associate with people who have become this way because of a sinful life."

In a recent interview his views were as positive and expressed with as much conviction as 15 years ago. It was his God-given duty to kill his persecutor, and although he promised not to attempt it again, duty at that time constrained him, and he believed that which he did was done by command and under guidance of the Almighty.

*Outstanding symptoms*:

(a)  Slow-growing, systematized delusions of persecution.

(b)  Feeling of superiority and perfection.

(c)  Unchanging character of the delusions.

(d)  Logical reasoning powers not affected.

*An extract from a letter* written by patient to his main (supposed) persecutor after the assault:

"Notwithstanding the fact that the trouble between you and me is not my problem, but God's, I will nevertheless write you, at the request of the doctor, the following words:

" 'Where I have been kept in the dark [everything is shrouded in mystery] as to who really can restore my liberty, you or the judge, I am willing to show myself the lesser and herewith request of you my release. Let God finally judge between us, in order that the right relation may maintain.' "

LETTERS WRITTEN BY MINISTERS relating difficulties with *Communicants* suffering from *Paranoid* delusions.

### (Case 11)

"Having had some strange experiences with a lady in this community, I am writing you for a bit of information and advice.

"She has, says she, had 'Spirit talking' with myself, and she resisted as long as possible, but at last my 'Spirit' compelled her to do my bidding. I was 'Always too strong' for her.

"For nearly three years she claims to have had those communications, and even traveled to Los Angeles to have Mrs. McPherson cure her of her enslavement to my 'Spirit.' She has spread (in a very narrow circle) the most absurd and shamelessly delicate lies about our family life, etc., upon these informing 'Spirit' talks.

"She formerly stated that 'my spirit' insisted that I marry her and that she hated me; yet she could not help defending me.

"On the other hand she acts in all other respects fully normal, and is the housekeeper for the family. Her evident sanity in other respects lends some plausibility to her claim to superstitious folk, although the few that know her are well aware of her irresponsibility."

## (Case 12)

"It began over two years ago with a telephone call during the week of preparation for communion in which she spoke in veiled terms, suggesting that I had been guilty of some misconduct. The whole thing mystified me and I told her that I would call at her home and she could explain herself. When I came she further mystified me by refusing to state what it was all about. She declared repeatedly, 'Oh, you know what it is.' And when I emphatically denied all knowledge of what she had on her mind she said, 'We'll leave it that way and just forget about it.' I went away perplexed, without the least idea of what she had on her heart.

"Some time later I had a similar experience. Again she called me up and when I went to her house to find out, if possible, what it might be, she received me in an agitated state of mind and again she would not tell me what it was all about. When I had declared myself wholly ignorant of what she had against me, she began to revile me, calling me a liar and denouncing me as a hypocrite and what not. All efforts to calm her and reason with her were of no avail.

"All this while I hadn't the least inkling of what her grievances might be, and could not even conjecture their nature.

"However, she did not keep me in the dark much longer. I began to receive letters falsely signed, and once she accosted me at the entrance of the church basement and launched out in bitter tirade. She accused me of casting amorous glances at certain women in the congregation from the pulpit, and even mentioned these by name. These charges were repeated in various forms with insinuations of immoral design."

## CHAPTER V

# Dementia Praecox (Schizophrenia)

*Dementia Praecox (early Dementia) or Schizo-*
*phrenia (Split Mind)*

THIS disease is more obscure, as far as origin and symptoms are concerned, than any other form of mental disturbance. Prof. Kraepelin of Munich named it Dementia Praecox, a name which indicates two important conditions of the disease. The first is that it occurs early in life; the second that it results in grave, permanent disturbance of all mental faculties.

As the disease may originate at any age and does not nearly always result in dementia, this term was considered less appropriate. In more recent years, Prof. Bleuler of Zurich named it Schizophrenia, meaning split mind. He considered the fundamental condition of this disease to exist in splitting of the personality. This term, superficially considered, has much in its favor as in this disease the unity and harmony of all mental activities and functions is, often for a shorter or longer period, seriously disturbed. It is my belief, however, that there is no evidence to prove a disturbance deeper than physiological processes. The personality, I am convinced, is a unit and not open to splitting or division.

Over 18% of admissions belong to this group. Of mental hospital population, 65% are schizophrenics.

The cause is obscure, but in many, hereditary factors are found.

The type of individual most frequently affected is the unsociable, shut-in type. Temperamentally, he may be either cold or sensitive, both qualities tending to isolation. Either society shuns him or he recoils from society.

Vague forebodings of gloom are often an early symptom of its insidious onset. The patient begins to complain of being tired and sits around staring, absorbed in his thoughts. If urged to work, he is irritable or becomes emotional. He laughs and cries without cause and may show no affection to those he formerly loved. Sleep is nearly always badly disturbed, but sleeplessness not complained of. Hallucinations of all senses are very common and often of an unpleasant, gruesome nature.

The almost numberless varieties into which this disease has been divided Kraepelin organized into four main groups, and authorities in general have followed his classification.

The four outstanding types are: simple, hebephrenic, katatonic, and paranoid.

## THE FOUR OUTSTANDING TYPES:

### 1. SIMPLE

This condition is characterized by a destruction of the whole psychic life and a course of events, so gradual, that even those of the patient's own household do not know when the disease set in.

The symptoms are about as follows: They begin to fail in school or other pursuits in which they were formerly successful. In early stages of the disease, the sufferer may make desperate attempts to regain his former initiative and ability to succeed. All attempts to overcome the crushing effect of the malady are, however, futile. The course of the disease is at times intermittent. Slowly there may be a partial restoration to normal mental functioning, but often the symptoms recur, making ever deeper inroads.

More advanced cases are emotional, irritable, indolent, and obstinate. The sympathy for others and attachment to the ones they previously loved, becomes dulled. Affection for parents changes to complete indifference or positive antagonism. The latter can probably often be explained as due to unkind treatment. They are misunderstood and their symptoms misinterpreted. For this reason they are scolded, threatened, and punished. They are accused of bringing the condition upon themselves by an immoral life. Masturbation, drinking, smoking, and the harboring of evil thoughts are especially considered the cause of patients' unusual reactions.

The final picture of these cases after years of suffering is one of complete indifference. There is no goal or purpose in life. The attachment to place and person vanishes. The tramp, beggar, alms house inmate, and prostitute, are often examples of its ravages.

## 2. HEBEPHRENIC (Insanity of youth)

It is similar to the simple dementia, and may appear as the final stage of that condition. Its onset is usually more acute and severe, however, and among the outstanding symptoms are hallucinations of all the senses and a strong delusional content.

The early symptoms are rather frequently a marked depressive episode, with religious or strong suicidal inclinations. It may also be ushered in by a period of extreme confusion. After the initial symptoms, the disease, if recovery does not ensue, follows a rather regular course.

The patient slowly secludes himself and if possible remains in bed entirely covered by blankets. He is disinterested in his surroundings, and love for relatives and former friends disappears. If not allowed to remain in bed, he seeks some secluded corner and sits there, often in the most awkward position. Outbursts of causeless, silly laughter, and weeping are common. If not molested the patients usually seem fairly well at ease, but if urged to change their position or to perform some duty, they become irritable and may fly into a rage. If they are willing to write, it will be noticed that the stream of thought has become irrelevant and incoherent.

The final picture is a condition of extreme deterioration, both physical and mental.

## 3. KATATONIC

As in the case of the hebephrenic types, the condition is often ushered in by a period of depression. The onset is, however, more sudden, and the early symptoms more suggestive of mental disease.

Many cases rather suddenly become confused and wander from home or take the train to some distant city. In this state they resemble the hysterical amnesias, but are, in contra-distinction to the hysterical fugeus, liable to become violent if restrained or urged to return.

In this katatonic condition, there is a strong and terrifying hallucinatory and delusional content. The period of excitement which may last from weeks to months, is followed by a condition of stupor. During this time, all voluntary movements cease, they neither walk, speak, nor eat. The thought processes are blocked, the muscles go into a state of waxy flexibility during which the extremities can be placed in any abnormal position and will stay there till changed (catalepsy).

The condition stands open to change, both emotional and physical. There are outbursts of sudden irritability and violence. A mute, negativistic, stuporous patient may suddenly run, jump, strike, kick or scream. One of our patients, quietly standing behind a 30-foot high building, suddenly ran as a human fly up the back of this building, and after arriving at the top, jumped down on an ash pile. Unharmed, he stood for a minute, then made a break for liberty, only to stop mute as suddenly as he had begun his dangerous ascent.

A typical case of katatonic dementia praecox does not evidence the extreme deterioration of the first two types. Behind that apparently impenetrable wall, the mental functions often remain fairly well preserved. I have seen these patients, after six years of extreme stupor, respond fairly well for short periods, both emotionally and intellectually.

## 4. PARANOID

This condition is as insidious as the simple form, but occurs late in life and may be secondary to the other types. It differs from pure paranoia and paranoid conditions in that it results in deterioration and has no systematized delusions.

After some 5 years, during which the symptoms are obscure and only recognized by those of their own household, the disease assumes more outstanding and dangerous proportions. The early symptoms of suspicion, ideas of reference, and persecution are intensified. The patient becomes irritable and threatening and seeks aid from governmental authorities against the imagined persecutors. Finally, outburst of rage, resulting from dreadful hallucinations, may drive the sufferer to acts of violence.

After this date, the course is usually variable. There may be weeks of calm and contentment, but these periods are often followed by days of extreme mental and emotional storm. A certain number become satisfied to live in a self-centered delusional world. One said to me, "If they call this crazy, I am entirely satisfied to remain this way." But there are others in whom for years and decades the delusional content periodically disturbs the patient.

## *ALL GROUPS*:

All types have a rather serious prognosis or outcome. After the first acute attack, there is usually a temporary recovery. In some 20 per cent of the katatonic, the patient's recovery is permanent.

As the attacks follow each other in a more or less rapid succession, the sufferer slowly deteriorates. This deterioration may show itself as years pass, both physically and mentally. The memory is, contrary to the impression left by the patient, not disturbed. He pays no attention to visitors and is not at all interested in his environment. The affective life is in many almost entirely destroyed. The paranoid type bears up best under the disease, and may even after years show very little change.

Treatment, in most cases, demands institutional care and protection to prevent suicide, homicide, etc. Isolation is dangerous. The patient should be kept, as far as conditions permit, in contact with the outside world and reality. The care of these patients during the early stage often demands the utmost tact, patience, and firmness. Graded work, after rest, should be encouraged. They must never be locked up alone, but should be kept with other patients. The presence of other mental cases, even if badly deteriorated, has a valuable restraining influence.

The shock treatment, produced by insulin, metrazol, etc., may give a new hope in the treatment of early cases of this dreadful disease.

### Schizoid: Hebephrenic Form (Case 13)

(a) *Hospital stay*: 15 years.

(b) *Duration* of acute psychosis: 5 years.

(c) *Outcome*: Marked deterioration.

She was a well-developed, quiet country girl, who a year before admission had become afflicted with a sense of heaviness and apprehension. More recently this depressed feeling became interrupted with short periods of silly laughter and an attitude of complete indifference. The periods of gloom of late had become more marked and a fear of death overwhelmed her. Palpitation of the heart and other strange bodily sensations increased her anxiety by day and unpleasant dreams terrorized her at night. Everything imaginable was tried to obtain relief, but of no avail. It is true, there were periods of remission, but these were usually short, and invariably followed by new attacks of greater severity than the preceding.

A longing for death to escape this unhappy existence tormented her. As by a mysterious hand, she was at times drawn to the quiet waters of a nearby lake. But life was still too dear, and suicide for her spelled eternal doom.

When questioned concerning her emotional life, she answered, "I feel awful. I cannot express it. I am afraid of everybody and nobody in particular. I fear death, but at times I wish to die. I may, however, not take my own life."

The last three months she spent at home, she sat for hours in one position, staring into space. If urged to work, she showed signs of irritability and at times became violent. Her nights were often sleepless and spent in roaming through the house, while during the day she frequently kept to bed, refusing to dress and assist with work. Attention to self and bodily needs were neglected. Although previously she was a model as concerned dress and general toilet, she was now indifferent

The food she ate was gulped down in haste and not obtained at the family board, but taken direct from the pantry and cupboard.

A letter written to her mother shortly after entering our hospital, gives insight into her mental content. The fact that this girl was reared in a home burdened by mystical religious tendencies, increases the picture of despondency from which she suffered, but on the whole the letter is a striking example of early depression found in many types of mental disturbance:

"I live," she wrote, "in a morbid state of mind, and to obtain relief from this I am writing you. An unexplainable obsession controls me, suggesting that I may not live, and a feeling of guilt because of my sins overpowers me. I scarcely dare speak to others. My conscience does not allow me. Just what the origin of these thoughts is, is a mystery to me. Whether God causes them to enter my mind, or the devil, I know not. I even fear to eat and I am not worthy to occupy the ground upon which I stand. The thought that is ever with me, is that I am lost. I scarcely dare to touch the Bible with my hands because I am sinful, but I do not dare to put it aside because of the judgment day. Whether God causes these thoughts to originate in my mind or whether my *weak nervous system* is at the root of the trouble, is not clear to me. At times I work desperately hard believing it to be my duty. But even this irritates me because I am convinced that work will not bring salvation. The words 'Not to the strong is the battle, nor to the swift is the race, but to the true and the faithful, victory is promised by Grace,' are ever with me. There are nights that I think I may not sleep and that I am not worthy to have a bed to rest on. But in turn my mind replies, 'It is within the providence of God that I was born, and for this reason he wants me to live and keep well,' for 'Not a hair can fall from our head without God's will.' The thought that I have sinned against you and the nurses also obsesses me, but this does not harmonize with the teaching that 'man can sin only against God.' It also occurs to me that I may not desire to be near you, mother, as you have also suffered agony of soul, but I believe mother is one of the elect. I do not dare express my feeling to the nurses as I consider myself too worthless. I do not feel this way the entire day, but nearly so.

"Your loving daughter."

This letter reveals little as to the seriousness of the mental disease from which she is suffering. There still is perfect logic in her thought processes. Her moods, although swinging between rather wide extremes may be within the range of normal, and the affective or love life expressed in her desire to be with dear ones, is entirely normal. The general course of the condition, however, points to the possible presence of a malignant mental disease, a disease which if it continues long or is severe, causes irreparable damage to the personality.

In order to prove to you that this patient really was suffering from symptoms of early mental disturbance, let me read to you parts of two letters written respectively three and six years after the above.

Three years have elapsed. She still stares into space, is indolent, indifferent about her appearance, and at times irritable and moody. A grave change, has, however, occurred in her mental life, as the following incoherent letter illustrates:

"Dear Friend:

"I am all set for a little fight in the best of time. It will be saved for them because then it is going to be all saved at the same time and it got fun on earth because it got most of fun with her baby darling again. It is better again it is too sad.

"Yours truly."

Another three years passed by, more stormy than the former. She has at times been violent, was always very confused and entirely indifferent as to her appearance. A note written at this time clearly illustrates all absence of logical thought sequence. Only disconnected words seem to fill her consciousness.
She wrote:

"candy candy Louis nervous letter jumped kind Miss candy lap no more Miss Massachusetts no more. Ida Clara Clara Ida I laughed I can't to write."

The final picture of this patient after an affliction of fifteen years can be best obtained from the monthly nurses' report: "Patient was dressed at 7 A.M. Fairly good-natured, but has irritable spells. At times troublesome and very restless [she will run about as if chased] but is usually silent, dull, indolent, contrary and resistive."

Hope for recovery in this patient is absent. She has undergone considerable deterioration and will never again fully appreciate social and religious values. But since the memory content is not affected, she may after the inward storm subsides, adjust herself fairly well in a protected environment, and to a degree find comfort and solace in the faith she once professed.

## SCHIZOID: HEBEPHRENIC, KATATONIC MIXTURE

### (Case 14)

(a) *Duration* of Condition: 2 years.

(b) *Outcome*: Social Adjustment.

*Extracts from letters*:

"I hope you are feeling fine, 'cause health means so much more than all the riches of this world.' I feel like I just lost completely everything, but will pray to our

Heavenly Father, who with His infinite love looks down upon His people. [She does her utmost to cling to her faith.] 'Whom have I Lord in heaven but Thee?' I can't remember the rest. I can't write much. It tires me too much. You'll have to excuse me. [The feeling of tiredness is often extreme in this type of mental derangement. It borders on exhaustion and is interpreted by the patient as a symptom of sickness.] I can hardly write. Can't sleep, can't eat.

"These voices [hallucinations] tell me everything I hear; I mean when anybody speaks to me, when they say nasty things [hallucinations frequently include thoughts relating to the reproductive functions.] It is getting worse all the time. When I write it makes me cry: also when I talk. [emotional instability] I never before [evidently refers to day-dreaming] saw things in my mind like I do now [hallucinations].

"I don't think there's any use in trying to get better because it seems like all my aunts and uncles and also the doctors that helped me are speaking to me. It's funny, but it's true. And that's what keeps going round and round in circles.

"When another patient hollers the same things goes through my mind and the same holds true when anyone talks to me. When I read letters their contents seem to be repeated in my head. When I move I can see myself move. When I go downstairs I can see myself upstairs, just can see myself being moved constantly."
[The whole represents a hyper-sensitive sensory and memory mechanism. Any wave set in action is repeated manifold. These waves may be set in motion by external forces as in reading, listening, movement, etc., or may originate in the memory sphere.

It is therefore rather important to keep such individuals in an environment that is unchanging, but they should never be allowed to be alone with their delusions and hallucinations.]

SCHIZOID: KATATONIC FORM. (Case 15)

(a) *Hospital stay*: 6 months.
(b) *Duration* of active disease: 4 months.
(c) *Outcome*: Mild deterioration (social recovery).

The patient was one of a family of nine. The grand-father died senile; an aunt was at one time mentally deranged, but the family in general was well-balanced, healthy, and thrifty.

Physically, he had always enjoyed unusually good health, but for the last few months complained of head-ache, dizziness and blurring of vision.

Socially, he stood aloof, but was regular in the attendance of meetings, both secular and religious. For the opposite sex he felt little attraction, in fact, soon was bored in the presence of women.

The past summer his relatives had observed a marked change in his views and habits. Whereas previously he had attended only the local church, he now began to neglect this church, and to frequent revival meetings. He also expressed unusual trends of thought. He said, "I receive visions from God urging me to become a missionary." A letter written at that time well illustrates these early symptoms. He wrote: "I desire to write father a letter to inform you that I am not busy with manual work, but desire to study the Bible, the Book. I study this to obtain wisdom of God and to gain strength and courage to preach woe to mankind." Shortly after writing this missive, he exhibited intense fear. He said, "The government is on my track and I will soon be put to death." He cried and prayed for hours, hid in the house and sought protection by police and church authorities. Food he refused, believing it to be poisoned, and his sleep was greatly disturbed.

In this condition of panic he entered the hospital, where during the first few days he showed marked improvement. The protection of closed doors apparently calmed his fearful mind and the presence of strangers stimulated him to control his delusional thoughts. This improvement, however, was of short duration. After a few days he sank into a deep stupor. This stupor was associated with rigidity of all muscles, and complete blocking of thought. He would stand speechless for hours in one and the same position. These periods of katatonic stupor were interspersed with occasional impulsive acts like striking, running, turning somersaults, screaming, etc.

Food he finally refused and had to be fed by tube. His bodily needs he ignored and was cared for as an infant during its first months of life.

After two months, this period of stupor, negativism, impulsive episodes, and irritability slowly cleared up. His confusion and fear subsided, he regained interest in his environment and work, and soon was able to return home.

His recovery was, however, not complete. The personality was warped. His affective or love life, his religious ideals, and altruistic desires were no longer as before the sickness. This lack came out clearly in a letter written to me sometime after his return home. And telling of his trip home and present activities, he ended the letter by expressing a desire to amass wealth. No word was written about relatives or friends, no greetings left to nurses who had cared for him, and not a single word expressing a desire that our work might prosper.

His life had become self-centered and devoid of warmth. Natural love for relatives had lessened, religious ideals became stagnant and altruistic motive vanished.

We have here the history of a healthy, energetic, reliable, conscientious young man, who, without evident reason, becomes afflicted with mental disease, passes through an acute, severe period of mental panic and recovers, but loses essential human traits.

What will be his future? Most cases of this type live a fairly well adjusted social life. In many there is, however, lack of contact. They live alone. Marriage they shun. Religious observance, if not entirely neglected, is no more than a routine. Interest on the whole is limited to physical animal needs. The tramp population and prostitute group find many in their camps that at one time suffered from this type of mental disease.

The seriousness of this type of mental disturbance is not to be sought in symptoms this disease may produce, but in the deteriorating effect on the organism. Some escape entirely unscathed, others, like our patient, show greater or smaller character deviations, and again others must be institutionalized the rest of their days.

## SCHIZOID: PARANOID TYPE  (Case 16)

*Extracts from letters.*

"Dear mother: I hear you are not feeling so well nowadays. I hope you will soon feel much better. Are the children much trouble to you? I would so love to care for them myself."

*Delusional* parts:

After asking some questions concerning their family history, she continues: "I know those questions sound funny, but there is a terrible funny sickness going around nowadays — radio sickness, they call it, and scientists are puzzling over it. I believe that radio is not as new as people have believed, but that some person who for years used it is becoming incautious because he thinks he is unconquerable. I believe my trouble was caused by the radio. I have found the names of mechanisms and what they do in the dictionary. I believe that somebody is so dead against the Christians that he or they are concentrating on them.

"That radio wave made me faint and gave me the notion I was being poisoned, and then because I was afraid of poison I did not dare to eat much, which made me weak and unable to do my work or think clearly. Then I heard voices, and I'm sure it came because of the radio. Then I was afraid to sleep. They gave me sleeping tablets and being weakened by lack of food, I talked a whole day feverishly and suffered from delirium. I still hear voices which I know by this time come from some radio machinery. I was just conscious enough last summer to realize that they were adjusting wires on some of the buildings here so they could keep me hearing voices and other patients, too, no doubt.

"One of these voices insisted that I commit suicide to rid my congregation of an incompetent. Why they were after me I do not know, but perhaps they are after my money. They say the most terrible things and show a person the most awful pictures, but I have found words in one of the latest dictionaries showing that there are machines that do such things.

"If you ever hear voices, don't worry and don't be afraid to eat. The radio waves tasted rather funny, coppery like, but it is not poison. A person needs a lawyer or detective rather than a doctor, seems to me.

"I at first suspected the doctor, but everything is so nice here and everybody so kind and considerate, that I began to think about it, and some of my thoughts are hard to explain, but due to the articles I find in the paper I believe I am on the right track. Some scientist, one or more, has gone mad with his invention, and is behind it all."

SCHIZOID: PARANOID TYPE (Case 17)

(a) *Duration*: Some 5 years.

(b) Personality well preserved. No signs of deterioration.

"I mistrusted my husband. I can't prove anything against him, but I know.

"I am not under any strain. I am just as healthy as anyone. I just should not listen to whispers I heard for a year. People can talk with their eyes. Thoughts are transferred from eyes. I thought long ago that I heard God's voice. I am sure I did. It happened about 3 to 4 years ago in the night. The devil does not talk much to me. Just before I left home, it was all microphones about the house. If I had a gun I would show the people who trouble me."

Patient at home periodically scolded and raved for hours; at other periods she was pleasant, clear, and sorry for attacks of violence.

The first few weeks at the hospital she was greatly relieved. The new impressions evidently ruled out the hallucinations, but before a month had passed, she wrote me a note stating:

"Dear Doctor:

"Will you please write to my husband and tell him I've got the same *terrible* problems here as what happens at home. She [the imagined persecutor] just keeps on concentrating on me, and hurting my head all the time. Please write my husband and tell him to take me farther away from home."

# CHAPTER VI

# Epileptic Psychoses

THE disease epilepsy (meaning to fall upon or being seized upon) has been a subject of rather wide discussion both in ancient and modern times. The sudden fall of an apparently healthy individual, accompanied by a weird cry, unconsciousness, and bizarre bodily contortions, made it ever a subject of wide interest. The disease has been ascribed to both good influences and bad, as a sign of being possessed by good spirits or devils.

We know today that the symptoms of an attack of epilepsy may be due to various brain diseases, but as concerns epilepsy proper or idiopathic epilepsy, the cause of this has thus far not been found.

The disease may be divided into epilepsy major, epilepsy minor or petit mal, and epileptic equivalents.

## I. EPILEPSY MAJOR (Grand Mal)

*Premonitory symptoms*:

It may be preceded for hours or days by slowly increasing restlessness, irritability, excitement, depression or confusion; or originate suddenly in a perfectly normal individual.

*Aura*: The seizures begin in about one-half of the cases by motor, sensory, or psychic aura. The patient may have sudden muscular contractions of momentary duration. The eye may observe flashes of light and the ear hear sounds evidently originating in space. A smaller group may experience a flight of ideas or impulsive thoughts. If the latter are present, the patient may become dangerous, attack people and destroy property.

*Unconsciousness and insensibility* suddenly follow. The patient drops to the ground and may be severely injured.

*Tonic phase*: (20 seconds to 2 minutes)

All the bodily muscles go into a tetanic rigidity. The chest wall is violently contracted, the larynx becomes fixed, and the result is the epileptic cry, shriek, or guttural sound. The bladder often empties, the mouth clamps shut and may injure the tongue, the fists curl, and cyanosis supervenes.

*Clonic phase*: (1 to 5 minutes)

The muscles relax only to again suddenly contract. The jaws grind, the eyes jerk sideways, the face presents hideous grimacing and there is an inco-ordinate jerking of the extremities. The saliva, which cannot be swallowed, is churned into foam and often colored red with blood. The clonic contractions slowly subside and the body for a shorter or longer period remains in a totally relaxed state.

*Period of Stertor*:

A stertorous breathing period, lasting some 5 to 10 minutes, usually follows. The patient then awakens, entirely unaware of what has happened.

*Post-epileptic state*:

This may last hours or weeks. The symptoms may be very similar to the premonitory phase, but more severe. There may be a mild confusion, depression, irritability, or a threatening attitude. The patient at times is decidedly dangerous, but most patients prefer to remain in bed, and if not disturbed quietly return to consciousness.

*Status epilepticus*:

In this condition there is a recurrence of a seizure before consciousness returns. These repetitions may be many. I have observed a patient going through as many as 240 longer and shorter attacks within 24 hours.

## II. EPILEPSY MINOR (Petit mal)

This condition should not be considered as an entity, but as part of a major attack. A flicker of light, a fall, or a spasm may present the attack. The most common symptom is a transient loss of consciousness. Patient turns pale, stares, and resumes his task where it was left off.

## III. EPILEPSY EQUIVALENTS. (Psychic epilepsy)

These resemble the aura, except that in these equivalents the patient does not remember what he has carried out. This is true, notwithstanding the fact that there is rational planning in the method of procedure. The sufferer may travel for days or weeks and not be recognized as abnormal; criminal acts may be carried out, as homicide, arson, sex crimes, etc.

*Conditions to differentiate epilepsy from:*

(a) Convulsions in children. These are often of no more import than shivering in grown ups.

(b) Fainting (Syncope). This patient falls, loses consciousness, has a feeble pulse, sweats, and is cyanosed, but has no convulsions, no tongue injury, no foaming at the mouth or emptying of the bladder.

(c) The following, although they have convulsions, can be distinguished by their history: hysteria, apoplexy or stroke, uremia, alcoholism, general paresis, meningitis, head injury, brain tumor.

*Course of the Disease:*

Fifteen per cent can retain important positions in life. Many, however, after some years show changes in the personality. Not a few become indifferent and careless about their own person, and show a very critical attitude toward their fellow-men. Slowly their range of interest narrows, which goes hand in hand with a strong egoistic tendency.

As deterioration proceeds, the memory becomes defective and judgment greatly impaired. Their conversation is irrelevant and circumstantial. A peculiar childish religiosity often prevails, probably caused by realization of impending death.

The danger to society of all individuals who suffer from convulsive disorders is first, death or injury to the patient himself during convulsions. They frequently are apparently unwilling or unable to take the necessary precautions. During the confused periods, they are often irritable and impulsive, and as they lack the normal inhibitory power, may make homicidal attacks. This disease should be kept in mind in all cases where crimes are committed with unnecessary violence.

*Treatment*:

Epilepsy is probably more a symptom than a disease, and can be caused by various conditions. This adds to the difficulty of treatment.

Regular hours, much sleep and rest, a moderate diet, avoidance of haste and undue stress and strain, are important. During the convulsions, protection is the only assistance and treatment that can be afforded. Certain drugs inhibit attacks and allay restlessness, and various diets of late years have been used which favorably affect the condition in certain patients.

# CHAPTER VII

# Psychoses with Psychopathic Personality

## (The borderline Psychoses)

### A. ANTI-SOCIAL PERSONALITY (Moral Imbecile)

THEY have no sense of responsibility and lack moral inhibitions. They steal, rob, commit crimes of violence, not only in the world about them, but in their very home, and never show sorrow or remorse for crimes committed. George stole the tires from his brother's car just before the funeral of his brother's child. There appears to be an early blunting or lack of development of the moral and emotional life, while the intellectual and physical growth is evidently normal.

### B. PATHOLOGICAL LIARS AND SWINDLERS.

They lie, steal, and cheat without purpose. Careful dress, a ready tongue, and an almost weird understanding of their victim's psychology make their success in the perpetration of fraud and deceit remarkable. Mild mania simulates this condition but is usually of shorter duration.

C. Paranoid Personalities: Cranks, Eccentrics, Ill-balanced.

They are like the paranoiacs, but have no delusions. They are egoistic, intolerant, suspicious, stubborn, argumentative, cynical, and faultfinding. They are often involved in litigation as they are determined to have "their rights." It is difficult or impossible for them to work in harmony with others. Closely allied to this group is "that host of ill-balanced eccentric individuals, who may be superficially brilliant, but lack continuity of purpose and capacity for continuous expenditure of effort in one direction. Their life, to use the well-chosen words of 'Regis' is one 'long contradiction between the apparent wealth of means and poverty of results'." (Jelliffe and White, p. 1137.)

D. Nomadic Personality.

Many of these are probably feebleminded or persons who suffered from a deteriorating psychosis. They lack all feeling of attachment to place, object, and person. They are aimless, restless travelers (Tramps).

E. Situational Psychosis (Prison Psychosis)

These psychoses may be characterized by confused states, excitement, depression, or paranoia, and brought on by great emotional stress. They are evidently limited to ill-balanced individuals or those who suffered from a previous attack of psychosis.

F. Sexual Psychopath.

Inability at adjustment early in marriage often points to sexual anomalies.

1. Quantitative anomalies:

> Frigidity of lack of desire.
> Eroticism, abnormal increase in desire.

2. Qualitative anomalies:

> *Inversions*:
>
> Homo-sexuality or desire for persons of same sex. This condition usually goes with physical anomalies.
>
> People suffering from this condition are some of the most pitiable human sufferers Their safety consists in choosing a social setting in which they are protected. Marriage in extreme cases should not be considered, but in the borderline group a good home life may be established, especially if the mate understands the abnormality from which the subject suffers.
>
> *Perversions.*
>
> a. *Masturbation*: (Self-abuse). This in itself, I am convinced, is never the cause of mental disturbance, nor is it an indication of a psychopathic constitution. It is, however, very common among psychopaths and the insane proper.
>
> b. *Sadisms* (Lust murder). The gratification of the sexual feeling by the infliction or sight of pain.

c. *Masochism*: The gratification of the sexual feeling by suffering pain. Flagellation was opposed by the Catholic church because of favoring this condition in certain nuns.

d. *Fetichism*: Sexual excitement and gratification by the sight of possession of some object or part of the body.

e. *Bestiality*: Sexual relation with animals.

f. *Exhibitionism*: Gratification by exposure.

g. *Scoptofilia*: Gratification by viewing the nude.

## *The responsibility of this group.*

Whereas in the psychoses proper the problem of responsibility usually brings up no question of dispute, this is not true of the cases we have just discussed. We find that the viewpoint of the public often depends upon whether the person is related to the so-called psychopath, or not. Near relatives will say, after comparing them with the world of people they are acquainted with, that they cannot be normal, and therefore cannot be considered fully responsible. Strangers, on the whole, judge them harshly.

There probably are in this group a mixture of cases very difficult to diagnose. Some appear to be individuals who at one time suffered from a mild form of mental disturbance, while others are high grade morons who superficially give the impression of being intellectually normal.

I am convinced that in the psychopath proper the lack of inhibition and the contra-social inclinations are often relative and not absolute. The knowledge that punishment is speedy and certain will in many instances protect these individuals from carrying out their wrong or abnormal inclinations and desires. In advanced cases, where prolonged nurture has resulted in ingrained habits and complete loss of inhibitory control, constant institutional protection is necessary.

# CHAPTER VIII

# Psychoneuroses and Neuroses

IN THIS group of conditions we meet with a milder disease entity. Its importance is, however, scarcely less than the functional mental diseases just studied, since it is unbelievably frequent, and the suffering to which it gives rise is scarcely less than in the major psychosis.

These diseases may appear as separate entities, but more often form a part of diseases in general. They often obscure both mental and physical maladies.

The attack upon the organism is different from that of the major functional psychoses. In these we find all the mental functions disturbed in the schizoid (Cases 13, 14, 15, 16, 17); the driving force mainly involved in the affective, manic-depressive psychosis (Cases 1, 2, 3, 4, 5, 6, 7, 8); and the judgment of self, the I, permanently warped in paranoia (Cases 9, 10, 11, 12). The psychoneuroses and neuroses present a struggle in the moral sphere associated with temporary or permanent superficial dissociation in cerebral structure or function.

Man is a responsible being and if his mind has developed normally, he recognizes himself as such. Deep in the personality rests the conviction of a positive good or right, and a positive bad or wrong. The "thou shalt" and "thou shalt not" of the ten commandments is engraved (although dimly) upon the soul of every human being. The normal individual, as he confronts life's problems and struggles, faces these squarely and either carries them out to the best of his ability or refuses to comply. He reasons, decides, and acts, either as his sense of justice directs, or he ignores this God-given guide and sins against "the light" God gave "every man that cometh into the world."

The psycho-neurotic does neither, but more or less unconsciously chooses a byway, and thus avoids a painful decision and an unpleasant or seemingly impossible task.

The methods unconsciously adopted are many, but outstanding examples are classified under the following heads:

A. PSYCHONEUROSES.

    I. Hysteria.

        a. Conversion of the mental struggle to bodily organ dysfunction.

        b. Temporary dream states or amnesia.

        c. Physical contortions during these dream states showing inner struggle.

        d. Incapacitation of the sufferer, or recovery.

    II. Psychasthenia. (Mind remains clear)

        a. Struggle not converted to physical symptoms, but evident in:

            1. Anxiety and fear of impending calamity or death.

2. Substitution of fear or guilt by obsessional, compulsive acts or thoughts.

## B. NEUROSES:

I. Neurasthenia. (Mind remains clear)

a. Preceded by true physical or mental exhaustion and fatigability.

b. Unconscious refusal or inability to accept defeat or to face difficult life situations.

c. Excitability of the special senses, favoring the origin of illusions as to bodily disease.

d. Phobias and anxieties.

They all have in common a limitation of interest as to the world in general, an intense focusing upon self, mental or physical, and a craving for attention.

*Hysteria.* (Case 18)

An intelligent, pleasant young woman of 30 periodically showed the following symptoms when her mind became obsessed with certain unpleasant thoughts. There was a change in the muscular tone. The sides of the mouth and shoulders drooped, the feet dragged and instead of walking briskly, she plodded. The extensor muscles seemed to overbalance the flexors, causing her to strike backwards. The pupils dilated, hearing gradually became lost, and the tone of voice changed.

Mentally, she fell into a dream state. Soon after this condition developed she would do one or more of the following:

1. Drop to the ground, become rigid, and twist in convulsive spasms.

2. Leave home and walk in this dream state for miles, finding her way along little known paths to some goal.
3. Tear up her garments or blankets, make a noose and attempt suicide.
4. Malign and ridicule hospital and nurses, and attack anyone who tried to detain her.
5. Wake up entirely unaware as to what had transpired.

*Outcome*: Recovery.

## *Hysteria.* (Case 19)

A young girl contemplated matrimony against the expressed wish of her parents. A prolonged period of struggle followed. Finally she planned the day of her marriage, unbeknown to parents and friends. As the day drew nearer, her panic in regard to this dilemma increased. She became ill and suffered severely from the following:

1. Nausea and vomiting.
2. Visual disturbance due to dilated pupils.
3. Choking sensations. A ball seemed to press within her chest upon aesophagus and respiratory organs.
4. Sensory disturbance.
5. Fear of impending death.

*Outcome*: Recovery.

## *Hysteria.* (Case 20)

A young poverty-stricken married woman faced what for her was an intolerable situation. She was forced to live in a tent. Money was lacking to buy the children food and clothing. Too proud to beg and ask favors of parents who had objected to marriage, she saw no way of escape. She developed pseudo-paralysis of the right extremity. From that date she used crutches for a period of two years. During these years there was a marked atrophy of disuse on the affected side. At the end of the two-year period her mind became deranged. She suffered from periods of excitement, during which both limbs again functioned normally. The crutches were then discarded and within two months she returned home well, both physically and mentally.

## Psychasthenia. (Anxiety type) Case 21)

A young man consulted a physician for palpitation of the heart. The physician found a minor blowing sound over the heart area and so informed the patient, advising as treatment some weeks of rest in bed. The patient went to bed, and became not only bed-ridden, but scarcely dared to turn from side to side. Fear of impending death overpowered him. In this state of anxiety his hyper-sensitive nervous system reported to the introspective mind various other signs. Besides the palpitation, he observed a constant throbbing of neck and abdominal bloodvessels and a distressing sensation of fullness in the throat, and pressure within the head. The relatives became alarmed and painstakingly complied with the young man's every want.

This condition of suspense continued until a specialist reversed the diagnosis. calling the heart signs functional. Recovery followed.

## Psychasthenia. (Obsessive Acts) (Case 22)

The compulsive acts of the psychasthenic are well illustrated by the washing of hands as performed by Lady Macbeth during a hysterical dream state.

The substitution of her guilt complex, a result of persuading her husband to commit murder, is the washing of hands. Here guilt is represented by blood and the handwashing is an expiation for sin committed.

## Macbeth Act V, Scene I

Scene I—Dunsinane. A Room in the Castle. Enter a Doctor of Physic and a Waiting-Gentlewoman.

Enter Lady Macbeth, with a taper.

Gent. This is her very guise; and, upon my life, fast asleep. Observe her; stand close.

Doct. How came she by that light?

Gent. Why, it stood by her: she has light by her continually; 'tis her command.

Doct. You see, her eyes are open.

Gent. Ay, but their sense is shut.

Doct. What is it she does now? Look, how she rubs her hands.

Gent. It is an accustomed action with her, to seem thus washing her hands: I have known her continue in this a quarter of an hour.

Lady M. Yet here's a spot.

Doct. Hark! She speaks: I will set down what comes from her, to satisfy my remembrance the more strongly.

Lady M. Out, damned spot! Out, I say — One; two: why, then 'tis time to do it; — Hell is murky — Fie, my lord, fie! a soldier, and afeard? What need we fear who knows it, when none can call our power to account? Yet who would have thought the old man to have had so much blood in him?

Doct. Do you mark that?

Lady M. The Thane of Fife had a wife; where is she now? —What, will these hands ne'er be clean? — No more o' that, my lord, no more o' that: you mar all with this starting.

Doct. Go to, go to; you have known what you should not.

Gent. She has spoke what she should not, I am sure of that: heaven knows what she has known.

Lady M. Here's the smell of the blood still: all the perfumes of Arabia will not sweeten this little hand. Oh, oh, oh!

Doct. What a sigh is there! The heart is sorely charged.

Gent. I would not have such a heart in my bosom for the dignity of the whole body.

Doct. Well, well, well, —

Gent. Pray God it be, sir.

Doct. This disease is beyond my practice: yet I have known those which have walked in their sleep who have died holily in their beds.

Lady M. Wash your hands, put on your nightgown; look not so pale: — I tell you yet again Banquo's buried; he cannot come out on's grave.

Doct. Even so?

Lady M. To bed, to bed; there's knocking at the gate: come, come, come, come, give me your hand: what's done cannot be undone: to bed, to bed, to bed.   (Exit.)

Doct. Will she go now to bed?

Gent. Directly.

Doct. Foul whisperings are abroad: Unnatural deeds do breed unnatural troubles: infected minds to their deaf pillows will discharge their secrets. More needs she the divine than the physician. — God, God forgive us all! — Look after her: Remove from her the means of all annoyance, And still keep eyes upon her: — so, good-night: My mind she has mated, and amaz'd my sight: I think, but dare not speak.

Gent.                                         Good-night, good doctor.
                                                        (Exeunt.)

The washing of the hands to erase guilt consciousness is a very common occurrence among mental cases both mild and severe.

*Psychasthenia.* (Obsessive *Thoughts*)

As obsessive, compulsive thought substitution we can consider: the counting mania, repetition of senseless or vile phrases, suggestive urgings to commit a crime, or immoral acts. The mind may be burdened with these for days and years, making life almost unbearable.

(Case 23)

A woman patient from morn till night was filled with the thought that she should marry another man, a man she had never spoken to, had only observed in passing, and for whom she harbored only disgust.

Just what these thoughts are substitutes of, is at times difficult to unravel, but many are substitutes for guilt, and express the need of atonement.

(Case 24)

A young barber, happily married but childless, soon after marriage became temporarily disturbed by the following obsession: At times when driving alone he would be forced to continue driving in one direction for varying periods of time. He could neither stop nor change his course until this idea ceased to control him.

After about 7 months, this obsessed idea left him and he lived a well-adjusted life for the next 9 years. At this time a more serious obsession overpowered him. While driving his car, an uncontrollable desire would manifest itself to self-exposure. He was apprehended and warned that life imprisonment in an institution for the criminally insane would result if this act was repeated. He suffered intensely, but finally was overpowered again by this obsession.

NEURASTHENIA. (Neurosis)

This condition is not due to a special happening in life, but occurs in predisposed individuals after prolonged trauma. This injury may be caused by excessive continued work, either mental or physical, or may result from worry over difficult life situations.

The sufferer is rather often an ambitious, persevering individual and the cause of the flight into this maelstrom may result from inability or unwillingness to accept defeat or failure.

The outstanding symptoms are anxiety, various phobias and innumerable unpleasant sensations referred to various bodily organs. These sensations to the sufferer present definite disease entities.

Those who suffer from this condition practically all complain of insomnia, dizziness and extreme fatigue after the slightest exertion. The symptoms referred to the bodily organs can be best classified as follows:

*Head*: This presents feelings of external pressure, a constricting band seems to encircle the head; or internal pressure, when a sense of bursting of the cranium annoys the sufferer. Headaches may be extreme and are often of a boring type. Stuffiness of the nose and pharynx suggest disease of the sinuses.

*The Neck and Back*: The upper part of the spine frequently has annoying symptoms of pain and pressure while the lower back presents a tired dragging sensation.

*Heart*: Its abnormal report is probably the main cause of the phobia of impending death. Its rate may be increased, decreased, or irregular, resulting in the sensation or cessation of action or fluttering. Pain about the heart may resemble angina and be associated with a bouncing against the chest wall that terrorizes the sufferer.

*Stomach and Intestines*: The appetite may be lost or greatly increased. Indigestion with gas formation may cause pressure against the diaphragm and result in the most annoying eructation of gas or hiccough. Nausea, vomiting, and diarrhea (mucous colitis) are common. Pain along the alimentary tract often simulates organic disease, suggesting cancer, ulcer, etc.

*Genito Urinary*: Impotence, dysparenia, dysmenorrhea, frequency of burning on urination, and fullness or throbbing in the lower abdomen.

*Chest*: Shortness of breath, pressure under the sternum causing distress or choking, result in fear of heart disease, tuberculosis, asthma, goitre, etc.

*Skin*: Sweating, flashes of heat, burning, itching and crawling are frequent sensation derived from the body surface.

In general they usually present an increased sensitivity towards all stimuli. There is intolerance to light and sound, while the sense of taste and smell may be exaggerated or perverted.

PHOBIAS:

Under this head are found such conditions as agoraphobia, or fear of open spaces; claustrophobia, fear of enclosures, etc.; further, fear of becoming insane, of losing one's memory, of impending poverty, and a host of other symptoms.

ANXIETIES:

As to anxieties, by which we understand fear without an object, these are similar to the condition described under Psychasthenia.

*Treatment* of the Psychoneuroses and Neuroses:

Before a method of treatment is instituted, it is necessary to make a careful diagnosis in order not to mistake this pseudo disease for a real malady. We must attack the possibilities involved by a process of elimination, as these conditions are often engrafted upon a real tissue disturbance. The psychoneuroses and neuroses usually present a rather weird multiplicity of symptoms and lack of definite, clear symptom-complex found in most known diseases, both physical and mental. This fact, together with a history of the case, usually makes it fairly easy to reach a conclusion.

Sad to say, not only the patient, but also the relatives often nourish the symptom, and the medical profession seems to repress the fact that these diseases are common. The result is prolonged treatment, and what was at first a mild condition results in an ingrained malady. The patient, due to the continued suggestion of disease, becomes more and more convinced that he is really suffering from a serious malady, and any attempt to uproot this error is met with violent opposition.

The physician frequently does not even need to prescribe a course of treatment. The patient is but too ready to suggest the most radical procedures. The desire to display symptoms is present in most cases. Surgery and hospitalization have a strong appeal. One of my patients had been operated on 19 times, and then turned to Christian Science. Thousands of these sufferers are treated daily for diseases of stomach and heart, sinuses and eye, uterus and bladder, and joint or muscle pains, by regular or irregular practitioners.

Many find temporary relief in all newer forms of treatment, but usually relapse when the fancy and excitement in the new remedy wears off.

Most of these patients would recover if they were made to see their problems in the early stage of the disease, but all will be greatly benefited if by a process of graded suggestion they can be made to see that they have unconsciously adopted the disease symptom. The desire to struggle against the odds and difficulties of life must be revived and a balanced life and world view fostered. Fundamental laws of being, evident in the reproductive urge, "Be fruitful"; constructive talents, "Subdue the earth and have dominion"; and moral and religious beliefs and longings, "For in Him we live and move and have our being," should be given attention proportionate to their individual intrinsic values.

Patients suffering from the neuroses should, in addition to mental suggestion, obtain a prolonged period of rest in a congenial environment. Sleep, rest, and nourishment over a period of months or even years is essential to complete recovery.

In the psychoneuroses, the problems are not so complicated, since bodily depletion is usually small or absent. But here the condition also may become chronic if the disease, instead of being correctly treated, is allowed to gain root. I cared for a person who during an attack of hysteria had become partly paralyzed and remained such for over 30 years, at which time an extensive atrophy made any attempt at recovery impossible.

These diseases are no respecters of persons. They are found among men as well as women, among the rich as well as the poor, and the ignorant are as subject to their ravages as the learned.

The value of some knowledge of the psychoneuroses can scarcely be overestimated.

A. It is the source from which the Freudian school obtained most of its interesting and valuable information, which interpreted by them, led to the formation of a one-sided, sex-centered life view.

B. In its light we obtain a better understanding of phenomena like hypotism, witchcraft, the present-day demon possession, etc.

C. Considered as a disease we find it not only occurring as an entity, but also as a frequent adjunct of other diseases, especially the chronic. Its presence may overshadow the physical disease to such a degree that when a patient is relieved of the suffering originating on the basis of the psychoneuroses and neuroses, he considers himself cured.

D. As to recovery, this depends in the first place, as in all other diseases, upon the restoring power God has placed in all human and living organisms. Where it concerns external healing forces, it is of inestimable value to the sufferer if the physician who treats him has insight into the condition, possesses a wholesome view of life, and true sympathy for the sufferer.

E. Its very common occurrence is one reason why there is more confusion, fraud, and deceit in the cure of human ills than in any other field of human endeavor.

# CHAPTER IX

## Psychoses with Mental Deficiency

MENTAL DEFICIENCY.

B Y mental deficiency we understand a delayed or arrested development of the mind, a deficiency in the potentiality for development which can never be overcome by education and training.

About one out of 60 in the population is subnormal. About one in 1,000 is institutionalized.

In 90% of cases of mental deficiency, the cause of the disorder is said to be hereditary. Other causes are disease of the mother, injury during labor, and further destructive processes in the brain or its coverings.

The mentally deficient are divided on the basis of their capacity to develop mentally. The *idiot's* mental age as compared to a normal child never reaches above *two* years; the *imbecile* may attain to the mental age of *six;* and the *moron* to the age of *twelve.*

The idiot, if not cared for, would perish.

The low grade imbecile may learn to feed himself, to read short words, and to perform simple tasks. Imbeciles of higher grade can do useful work and learn to protect themselves in society.

As to the morons, it may never be realized by their community that they are mentally defective. The lower grades can use machines and do unskilled labor. The higher grades are self-supporting and can at times only be diagnosed by their reactions under conditions of abnormal stress and strain, and by their lack of ability to comprehend the broader problems of life.

If protected and carefully trained when young, the higher grades of the feebleminded can assume fairly responsible positions in life.

It is not true, as at times stated, that mental defect implies criminal tendencies. Many feebleminded are conscientious and law abiding citizens. It is true, however, that the percentage of defectives in jails and penitentiaries is considerably higher than in the general population. It ranges from 10 to 21%, as compared with less than 2% in the general population.

Marriage among the mentally defectives should be prohibited, as mental defect is often strongly hereditary. A father and mother feebleminded practically always results in an entire family of defective children.

Great caution must be exercised lest the diagnosis of mental defect be mistaken. The apparent mental defect may only be a retardation due to external or internal cause. Some individuals develop slowly. Further, an unfavorable environment may have a marked inhibitory effect upon the normal development; and lastly, bodily disease or absence of one of the special senses may result in mental conditions greatly resembling feeblemindedness.

The prognosis of all true cases is naturally hopeless, as the native intelligence in a human being is fixed.

# CHAPTER X

# Traumatic Psychoses and Psychoses with Brain Tumor

THE relation of trauma to the psychoses can be considered from three viewpoints.

I. A psychotic condition may result in trauma. Mental patients rather frequently commit acts of violence due to hallucinations and delusions. I recently admitted a patient suffering from an acute psychosis who had injured his back by jumping through an open window. The relatives believed that the psychosis was due to the injury, but fact was that he had suffered from peculiar dream states for days. This individual presented a typical case of katatonic dementia praecox and beyond doubt had jumped from the window to escape some imagined danger.

II. Bodily injury may result in a situational psychosis or precipitate a latent psychosis. The depressing and exciting factors that accompany severe injuries are many. Pain and suffering, prolonged hospitalization, legal complications, insurance claims, etc., are incidents that may deplete bodily reserve and stir up an emotional stress far beyond the endurance of certain predisposed individuals.

A man of about 55, an ambitious regular laborer, fell from a roof he was shingling, and injured shoulder, head, and neck. X-rays were taken and careful investigation made by competent physicians, but no serious condition found. He was advised to discontinue work and obtain several weeks of rest. But about a month after the injury, he developed a marked personality change, presenting all the symptoms found under involution melancholia. A latent psychosis had been precipitated by a relatively mild injury.

III. Trauma may also cause damage to brain tissue and thus bring about a psychosis.

Trauma is frequently presented by relatives as a direct cause of mental derangement, but a careful consideration of the case usually rules it out. The frequency of auto accidents has of late years increased the cases suffering from traumatic psychosis, but even now the number is well under one per cent.

Immediately after a severe brain injury there is often clouding of consciousness, memory loss for the event, dizziness, vomiting, and, if serious, coma. Unless there is positive compression of the brain due to skull fracture, these cases are today treated expectantly. Rest in bed, quiet, exclusion of visitors, and a restricted fluid diet, are of the greatest importance until symptoms subside.

In the more severe cases there is, due to destruction of brain tissue, a sequence very serious in prognosis. This may exist in permanent psychotic symptoms or milder disorders, as, memory defects and inability to perform efficiently one's previous occupation. It also may become apparent in motor involvement evident in convulsive phenomena or paralysis.

A boy of 13 one night on his way home from school received an injury due to falling in a gravel pit. He was found unconscious and remained such for 3 days. A week after the fall he began to suffer from speech defect (aphasia) and paralysis (hemiplegia). This whole picture slowly cleared up except for some weakness on the affected side, mental unrest, and irritability, followed after a period of two years by Jacksonian epilepsy (convulsions beginning in the affected side and extending over the entire body) and definite mental disturbance.

The brain injury obtained in the fall caused not only a partial paralysis and a convulsive disorder, but also positive psychotic symptoms.

PSYCHOSIS WITH BRAIN TUMOR.

The symptoms of this condition usually come on very slowly. The patient complains of increasing headaches, dizziness, vomiting, loss of vision, drowsiness, etc.

Mental symptoms are rare, but there may be a change in the personality, memory failure, irritability, suspicion, ideas of persecution, and lastly a profound dementia.

# CHAPTER XI

# Psychoses with Other Brain and Nervous Diseases

ENCEPHALITIS — LETHARGICA.

## (Sleeping sickness, probably always secondary to Influenza)

THE early symptoms are headache, fever, sleep disturbance (sleepless or sleepy), double vision, apathy, delirium, fatigability, and depression. There are various personality changes. Children, as well as older people, may become unmanageable, assaultive, annoying, restless, and may also develop serious physical signs and symptoms.

After a shorter or longer period signs and symptoms develop which resemble those found in Parkinsonian disease, (shaking, palsy, paralysis agitans). There is muscular rigidity, which gradually results in contractures and atrophy. The face becomes expressionless, the eyes stare straight forward into space (masked facies). The tongue may protrude and hang from the mouth as if paralyzed and disturbance of the muscles of deglutation causes the saliva to run freely from the open mouth.

The fingers are usually extended and assume a pill rolling position. There is a continuous tremor, especially of the hands, which can be voluntarily controlled for short periods. The patient walks semi-stooped and drags his feet. Flexion and extension of thigh and leg are almost absent. As if in fear of falling forward, he runs, and when once in motion may have great difficulty in coming to a halt.

Gradually the patient becomes bedridden. The hands and feet, due to the continual spasm, assume abnormal positions, making all movement difficult. Voluntary activity gradually becomes impossible, but involuntary spontaneous movement may remain present for years. To demonstrate: A young patient of 20 who had been afflicted for years and had great difficulty in getting about, fell against a radiator and was severely burned. Notwithstanding the pain it was impossible for her to bring voluntary muscles into action. This same person would, when emergencies arose, spontaneously carry out rather complicated activities. To assist a nurse who was attacked by another patient, she suddenly left her bed and turned in the alarm, but after this was accomplished, she fell and was unable to return to bed.

Institutional care and protection often becomes necessary, notwithstanding the fact that the patient remains intellectually clear and retains good insight into his condition.

There is a strong hysterical element in many of this class of cases, which can be greatly reduced by wise guidance and regular institutional life.

Hope for complete recovery is poor as there is usually a wide, extensive involvement of brain tissue.

Medication: The atropine series affects many of these patients favorably.

## CHOREA (ST. VITUS DANCE)

The physical signs are irregular, purposeless, involuntary movements.

The child suffering from this condition slowly develops a peculiar clumsiness and some character change. He drops dishes, is self-willed, peevish, irritable, fearful, and "scatter-brained." Early cases are often not recognized and frequently punished by teachers and parents.

Recovery is the rule, but the child needs quiet, rest, and the protection of a sympathetic home.

CHAPTER XII

# Psychoses with Other Somatic Diseases

PNEUMONIA, TYPHOID, HEART *and* KIDNEY DISEASES, *as also cases of* EXTREME EXHAUSTION.

THESE diseases sometimes bring on psychoses. The symptoms are a clouding of consciousness, illusions, hallucinations, and finally confusion and amnesia. If the psychosis is mild the patient can be aroused when spoken to, but in the more severe conditions it is not possible to awaken him. The patient often is restless, fearful, and cunning. Escape from caretaker is frequent and accidents resulting from such escape common.

At night the delirium is often more marked. In terminal cases the patient often mutters to himself, pulls at the bed clothes, and finally sinks into a deep stupor.

PSYCHOSES DUE TO DISTURBANCE OF THE ENDOCRINE GLANDS.

The body has some ten glands called internal secretory or endocrine glands. Knowledge of these glands is recent, but the amount of work done to clarify their purpose and function is great. They exert a marked effect upon bodily growth and function. When diseased or absent, either at birth or during life, the resulting defect in the organism, both physical or mental, is marked. Knowledge of the subject is still fragmentary, however, and incomplete.

The gland best known is the thyroid. This gland is located on both sides of the larynx, in the neck, and when diseased gives rise to such conditions as toxic and simple goitre, and when absent or deficient to dwarfism or myxedema. In myxedema or thyroid deficiency, there results slowness of all psychic processes, impairment of memory, loss of interest, listlessness, sleepiness, etc. Hallucinations and delusions may appear but are not common.

In hyper thyrodism (exophthalmic goitre) the symptomatology is just the reverse. In the more severe cases there is present extreme excitability and irritability. The symptoms in a few simulate the manic depressive psychosis. As to whether the hyperactivity of the gland is the cause of these symptoms or results from the excited condition from which the body in general suffers is in early cases difficult to determine.

When the gland is absent at birth, we get a certain type of dwarf called the cretin. This patient develops neither physically nor mentally. The feeding of the glandular extract to these patients may result in a marked improvement both physically and mentally.

The science of endocrinology, together with that of the body chemistry, may in the future throw much light on obscure problems in the field of mental disturbance.

# CHAPTER XIII

# Psychoses Due to Drugs and Other Exogenous Toxins

### MORPHINE ADDICTION

OPIUM (morphine, heroin and codein, are its active principles).

Its continued use results in a gradual disintegration of the personality and character. The addict becomes self-centered, indifferent, untruthful, unreliable, and neglects family and home.

When deprived of the drug he is tremulous, restless, irritable, anxious, — in one word, indescribably uncomfortable; but as soon as the drug begins to re-exert its influence, a sense of ease and well-being slowly replaces all the agonizing sensations.

### BROMIDES

Any one of this class of drugs when used over a long period of time may cause a clouding of consciousness, delirium, disorientation, and hallucinations.

### LEAD POISONING

This condition originates in people who work with lead for long periods and do not take the necessary precautions. (Plumbers, painters, printers, etc.)

*Symptoms*: Intestinal colics, headaches, neuritis and paralysis of the extremities. In the final stages lead poisoning may resemble alcoholic poisoning.

## MARIHUANA (Canabis Sativa, or Hemp)

This is a drug used extensively all over the world. In this country it is almost always taken in the form of cigarettes that contain the drug. Such cigarettes are often sold by unscrupulous vendors to high school children who, though unwittingly, soon become addicted to the drug.

Like alcohol and morphine this drug gives the addict a feeling of well-being, and depresses his inhibitions. The result is moral misconduct and a condition of excitement, during which the addict may become dangerous. The excitement is followed by a period of stupor.

## PATENT MEDICINES

These may contain habit-forming drugs and give rise to mental symptoms. It is dangerous to use any drug over a long period of time, unless such use is prescribed by a qualified physician.

# CHAPTER XIV

# Alcoholic Psychoses

IT IS generally conceded that alcohol is a powerful poison, and as such, if taken in large quantities or over long periods of time, produces serious damage to the individual. The toxic properties of alcohol far outweigh any possible beneficent effects it may have." (Jelliffe and White, *Diseases of the Nervous System*, p. 1062).

The habit-forming element in alcohol evidently rests upon a different factor than that present in the opium series. The alcoholic can be easily weaned from the use of the drug. No serious physical symptoms follow immediate removal. In my patients I invariably find that after the toxicity due to alcohol is eliminated, (up to this point there apparently is a demand) they feel perfectly at ease and neither ask for nor crave the drug. In the morphine addict, sudden total removal, however, causes serious physical symptoms and extreme mental unrest.

Evidently the use of alcohol tends to become habit-forming, not, as commonly believed, because the body acquires a need for the drug, but because of psychological factors.

The feeling of well-being alcohol produces and its power to repress unhappy thoughts are evidently outstanding reasons why the alcoholic wants the drug. This, however, does not explain all the symptoms from which the alcoholic suffers. There indeed is a physical factor in the chronic alcoholic. The cerebral tissue slowly becomes injured and this has a serious effect upon the personality. The inhibitory control is lowered, the emotions become unstable, and the sense of responsibility is impaired.

Although the habit-forming factor in alcohol addiction is not as serious as in the morphine addict, the final result is almost identical. Both will lie, steal, and kill to obtain the drug; both often go on until disability or death ends their career.

As the alcoholic is, however, more easily weaned from the use of the drug, hope for recovery is far greater than in the opium addict. If only the brain tissue is not injured beyond repair, a favorable environment and strong moral stimulus can do much to aid in readjusting a relatively severe case of alcoholism.

## DRUNKENNESS

It is a temporary state in an individual who has used alcohol to the extent that toxic symptoms result. The mood in these individuals varies. They may be talkative, euphoric, and over-active, or sullen and morose, and seek relief in isolation and quiet. The judgment is clouded and inhibition lost, causing the individual to transgress moral and civil laws. As the motor centers become affected, co-ordination is lost. The drunk-

ard sways and, finally, unable to maintain his equilib-
rium, slumps to the ground. After a vain effort to
arise, he may sink into a deep sleep. As the sensory
centers are also disturbed, neither inclement weather
nor the cold or rough and hard surface upon which he
lies awakens him.

## Chronic Alcoholic

The mental change in this patient is gradual and
progressive. The intelligence becomes blunted, the
judgment impaired. His moral sense is dulled and
delusions often develop.

To the public he gives the impression of being big-
hearted and a jolly good sport. In the home he is
brutal and shows no consideration for parent, wife, or
child. To still his unquenchable thirst he pawns his
children's clothing, and the money needed for food. If
reprimanded during lucid periods he is sentimental,
promises reform and begs forgiveness. The moral fiber
is often so badly affected, however, that the personality
is broken and hope for improvement very small.

## Korsakow's Psychosis

This is a psychosis found in association with alcoholic poly-neuritis, and is not limited to mental disturbance arising from alcoholic poisons. The form due
to alcohol often arises after attacks of delirium and is
at times considered a chronic delirium.

There is a memory defect for present events which
is partly due to lack of attention. Hazy memory pic-

tures are filled with fabrications. The stories the patients tell on the basis of such distorted memories are of the most absurd and impossible nature.

I cared for a patient some years ago, who after suffering for a year from extreme alcoholic neuritis (pain along nerve trunks) began to fabricate in connection with dream memories. Although wide awake, he would relate stories he had evidently dreamed, stories about horses he had driven the past night, logs he had hauled and beer parties he had attended. He gradually became entirely paralyzed and extremely confused, and died in convulsions.

The life history of many chronic alcoholics shows them to have been individuals quite incapable of meeting reality efficiently. In alcohol they found an escape from the problems of life.

### DELIRIUM TREMENS (Snakes)

An acute psychosis caused by an excessive ingestion of alcohol in a chronic drunkard. It often follows accidents, infections, surgical operations and acute diseases.

The outstanding symptoms are delirium, and hallucinations of a fleeting nature. The hallucinations are usually of vision and frequently in motion; running mice, crawling bugs, etc.

### TREATMENT OF ALCOHOLISM:

1. Drugs do not cure alcoholism. Although drugs and vitamins may be of aid in the restoration of bodily

health, they do not cause an aversion towards alcohol, or affect recovery directly.

2. Value of institutionalization.

a. This gives the body an opportunity to eliminate alcoholic poisons, to restore normal metabolism and to rebuild injured tissue.

b. Deprivation of liberty (6 months to 2 years) has a moral value as it impresses upon the addict the seriousness of his condition and gives him time to reflect.

c. It affords an opportunity to teach him fundamental facts as to the effect of alcohol upon the body with resulting physical and moral disintegration.

PROGNOSIS or hope for recovery.

1. This depends upon the physical, moral, and mental integrity of the addict.

2. Total abstinence is imperative.

# CHAPTER XV

# General Paralysis and Psychoses with Cerebral Syphilis

GENERAL PARALYSIS:

THERE are two common venereal diseases. The one, gonorrhea, is caused by a biscuit-shaped organism, the gonococcus. A profuse urethral discharge often begins shortly after infection and lasts some three or four weeks. It frequently becomes chronic, however, and then causes endless suffering in both male and female. It does not cause insanity except for a possible acute delirium.

The other venereal disease is syphilis. It is caused by a cork-screw shaped organism, the spirochita pallida. This last disease is a frequent cause of mental disturbance. It runs its course in stages.

The first stage begins after an incubation period of about three weeks. The earliest lesion noticed is an indurated single sore. It contains millions of bacteria and is extremely contagious. If on the lip it may be transferred by drinking cup, kissing, etc. Its spread usually results from illicit relation, and an infected individual frequently transfers the disease to the mate.

The chancre, as the lesion is called, heals in about a month, but is followed, if not thoroughly treated, by a multiplicity of lesions spread over the entire body. This second stage may last one or more years, and ends in a quiet phase. During this last period all symptoms are absent but the spirochite lives on hidden in some undetermined location. This is followed by a third stage which may, if untreated, last years and affect any bodily organ or tissue.

In about 5 to 10% the nervous system is involved. If this occurs the disease is very resistant to treatment and follows an insidious malignant course. It may involve:

I. The spinal cord and extend upward involving certain cranial nerves. If this happens it is spoken of as locomotor ataxia (Tabes Dorsalis). The disease then gives rise primarily to the following signs and symptoms:

A. Sensory disturbance.
    a. loss of vision.
    b. excruciating transitory pains below the waist line (gastric crisis).
    c. loss of sensations as to the position of the limbs.
    d. analgesia (loss of sense of pain over certain skin areas).
    e. exhaustion after minor effort.

B. Motor disturbance.
    a. paralysis of the muscles controlling the eyeballs and lids.
    b. paralysis of the muscles of the extremities, especially the lower.
    c. the paralysis of all muscles and wasting of the muscles.

C. The Mind remains clear.

II. The meninges, and extend into brain along the blood vessels. This condition may supervene at any time after the healing of the chancre and therefore includes both the second and latest stage of syphilitic infection.

Signs and symptoms.

    a. headache, sleeplessness
    b. dizziness, nausea, vomiting
    c. diminution of visual acuity or blindness
    d. paralysis of eye and facial muscles
    e. defective hearing or dizziness
    f. mental apathy or coma
    g. violent delirium
    h. epileptiform convulsions
    i. speech involvement, slurring, stumbling, etc.
    j. hemiplegia and aphasia
    k. hemianesthesia
    l. sudden temporary recovery

III. The brain tissue proper (Parenchyma).

Paresis: general paresis, dementia paralytica, general paralysis of the insane. (Stedman)

About 12% of all patients that enter our large state hospitals suffer from this disease, and from 2 to 5% of individuals that acquire syphilis, develop paresis.

The early symptoms of paresis include a slow change in the personality. There is a failing of efficiency, irritability, memory disturbance, and often some depression. In not a few the first thing that attracts public attention it a gross breach of some moral standard. The onset is at times so slow and insidious, however, that the condition is not recognized for some two to six years.

A fully developed case often presents very characteristic symptoms. A strange feeling of well-being slowly takes possession of the patient. He has unlimited self- confidence and grandiose delusions of wealth and power, which may alternate with periods of extreme irritability and depression. With a broad, beaming smile he greets strangers and neighbors, while the members of his own household are treated with irritability and gloom. Ideas of persecution are usually present and may cause the patient much suffering as consciousness may remain clear for years.

The outcome in untreated cases is usually fatal in from two months to ten years. There are frequent remissions, however, during which the patient is relatively normal and at ease, but each attack increases the physical and mental deterioration, until at last the picture ends in entire paralysis or convulsive seizures.

The fever treatment has for the last ten years made the possibility of recovery for these cases much more hopeful. All cases of paresis should immediately receive this treatment in a well-equipped mental hospital. About 20% after such treatment recover sufficiently to resume their former occupations, and about 40% again adjust themselves either in society or to hospital routine.

The problem the general paretic presents in society may be marked. They are usually irritable and restless, and their delusions result in antisocial conduct and homicidal assaults.

The following is the history of a man who acquired syphilis in youth and died of paresis.

### (Case 25)

*A successful business man.*

He lived in a beautiful home among the well-to-do of his town. A successful business career had been his; where others had failed, he had won. He was highly esteemed by his neighbors. In all civil affairs his judgment was valued. Physically, he appeared the picture of health: robust, tall, and well-nourished. It is true his deepset eyes at times showed worry, and his forehead was deeply wrinkled. But this could be expected, for competition was keen and his field of labor difficult and wide.

One evening, after a hard day's work, he returned home deeply troubled. For the first time today he noticed that his vision was failing. Carefully he tried to hide his feelings from wife and children. These had, however already for weeks noticed a slow change creep over his usual pleasant and open character.

The disease these symptoms resulted from was acquired in youth.

*A Youth in His Prime.*

With great tenderness and pride a mother assisted her son in preparing himself for an evening of pleasure. He was the apple of her eye, an only son, the pride of a respectable family.

He went that evening to enjoy the pleasures of the world. His mother expected him to attend some harmless entertainment, but he strayed that night. With friends he passed a dance hall, adjoining a saloon and

house of ill fame. They entered. The strong drink
clouded his mind; the dance aroused his passion. (Prov.
7) "With her much fair speech she caused him to yield,
with the flattering of her lips she forced him away. He
goeth after her straightway as an ox goeth to the slaugh-
ter, or as a fool to the correction of the stocks; Till a dart
strike through his liver; as a bird hasteth to the snare,
and knoweth not that it is for his life. For she hath cast
down many wounded: yea, all her slain are as a mighty
host. Her house is the way to Sheol, going down to the
chambers of death."

In the early morning he returned home and quietly
stole to his room. For two years the result of this sin
haunted him. The disease (syphilis) he had contracted
that night was stubborn, and responded poorly to treatment. After this period his health returned, his spirit
and ambition revived. He married into a respectable
family, became a father of healthy children, and succeeded in life as we saw above.

*Days of Remorse.*

He had erased from conscious memory all thoughts of
the dreaded disease. The doctors had pronounced him
cured and for over twenty-five years he had been healthy
and strong. But now, when life's success reached its highest peak, retribution found and punished him. Headaches, at times almost unbearable, began to trouble him.
His vision became dimmed, his gait uncertain; and what
was most serious of all, his strong will, well-balanced
emotion, and clear intellect seemed out of adjustment.
Medical advisors told him what he but too well knew,
and promised little hope. They ordered rest, but for
him there was no rest. In the dead of the night, he left
his home and wandered to the grave of his mother. In
the agony of his soul he cried, "Oh, what a shame! Had
my mother known this! If it was only not my own
fault! Would that I had never been born!" He feared

the death he longed for, and prayed as he never prayed before. The days became weeks, the weeks months, and finally the struggle ended.

*A Living Death.*

They took him from home. His anguish had turned to indifference; the cry for mercy to hollow laughter, and his feeling of inability and weakness to strange thoughts of power, riches, and strength. The ones he loved most he now threatened and reviled.

The next three years he spent in confinement, blind to the condition and the realities of life. He boasted of millions and miraculous creative powers; and possessed a feeling of well-being far beyond what he had ever experienced before, and finally the tragedy ended when death claimed the body of which the mind had gone before.

## *General consideration of syphilis:*

A. This disease can be diagnosed by examination of the blood and spinal fluid.

B. Early treatment is of the utmost importance. There is medicine that will result in recovery if the general nervous system is not involved.

C. If the nervous system is involved, fever treatment should be given. (Induced by malaria or a high temperature producing apparatus.)

D. Syphilitic sores are very contagious the first two years after invasion.

E. Syphilis in the mother is rather frequently transferred to the children, resulting in defective offspring. (Hereditary syphilis. Juvenile paresis.)

F. Syphilis in the father, if in the third stage, is usually not transferred to the mate and never directly to the offspring.

G. Patients suffering from paresis or juvenile paresis do not spread the disease.

H. The fact that the spirochite, as nearly all other germs, lose their virulence very soon after exposure to air, limits contagion almost entirely to direct contact of tissues. Drinking cups, fountains, etc., can only serve as a media of transfer if contact is made within a few minutes after diseased tissues harboring the virulent organism have touched the vessel.

# CHAPTER XVI

## Psychoses with Cerebral Arteriosclerosis

ARTERIOSCLEROSIS consists of a stiffening of the arterial wall due to loss of the elastic element and deposition of material which is non-elastic.

As to the ultimate cause of this condition there is still much doubt, but in addition to advancing years there is evidence to prove that heredity, syphilis, alcohol, chronic diseases (heart and kidneys), as also emotional stress play an important part.

Its time of onset is about the end of the fifth decade. It follows general paralysis which usually becomes evident in the latter part of the fourth decade and precedes senility in which it often is present.

If the larger blood vessels are mainly involved, there is a break in their walls or thrombus (clot) formation causing a rather large brain area to be thrown out of function. The result then usually is partial paralysis (hemiplegia), speech involvement (aphasia), and temporary loss of consciousness. This condition is designated as apoplexy or stroke. All symptoms may be transient and mild, or permanent and fatal.

The body is usually able to re-establish the circulation and to restore brain nourishment. After a few days or weeks, consciousness is regained and muscular movement returns to normal. There is, however, a wide range of possibilities between total recovery and death. The patient may remain confused, hallucinated, irritable, or totally paralyzed and extremely sensitive to touch, and live on in that condition for months or years.

When the smaller vessels are mainly affected, the destructive process is usually much slower and the onset of symptoms more gradual. The early complaint in these patients is headache, dizziness, irritability, memory gaps or loss, emotional instability and suspicion, directed especially against those of the household. Those symptoms may be followed by more serious indications of mental diseases, as contrasocial conduct and delusions of depression and persecution. Physically, there is often, but not necessarily, an increase in the blood pressure and if the case is rather advanced, motor and sensory signs may supervene.

Notwithstanding these serious organic symptoms, White claims that the "nucleus of the personality is often well preserved." The deterioration observed in the senile and the general paretic is usually absent. This is probably due to the fact that the condition is not general, but localized in certain brain regions.

The prognosis in most cases is serious, as what is destroyed in the brain or nervous system, is never restored. In cases of apoplexy, it is possible, however, to have a perfect and lasting recovery. One of my patients had no recurrence for some 35 years after the first apoplectic stroke. During all these years he lived an active, useful social life, and had positively no abnormal symptoms until two years before a second attack.

As to dangers to society and self, this varies much, but since the progress is slow, there is ample opportunity to recognize abnormality and protect the individual and society.

## (Case 26)

*Occupation*: Mechanical engineer and inventor.

*Age*: At onset of symptoms, 57.

At date of admission, 65.

Patient visited some 50 different physicians, both regular and irregular, but sought in vain for relief.

(1) Eyegrounds as reported by Mayo Clinic and Ann Arbor Univ. Hospital showed sclerosis and reduction in size of retinal vessels.

(2) Blood pressure was increased. Superficial arteries tortuous.

(3) Disturbance of sensation and sensory organs: pain in head, back, legs, and over the sciatic nerve. Tingling and numbness of the toes and finger tips. Temporary loss and blurring of vision. Ringing in the ears.

(4) Paranoid symptoms.

Had an exaggerated opinion of self and harbored ideas of persecution and suspicion against those of his household. He was critical, bitter, and revengeful toward his daughter, and jealous of affection she bestowed upon her children. His son he accused of mocking him by word and deed. Said, "John imitates my moaning and peculiar actions. All they want is my money and property." (Fact was he had spent it all in seeking relief.)

(5)  Periods of depression.

He suffered from restlessness and great anxiety and attempted suicide by shooting, hanging, cutting arteries, poisoning, and jumping from window.

(6) Loss of consciousness or mild epileptic attacks. "Flashes go through my head. I am powerless during these seconds."

(7)  Narrowing of the field of interest. His conversation was practically limited to expression of bodily suffering and complaints against his children and society.

(8)  Somatic complaints.

These may to some extent have had a delusional origin but were probably mostly due to sclerosis in the sensory area.  He almost continuously moaned and groaned and complained of pain in bowels, stomach, head, back, etc. That these expressions of pain were greatly exaggerated and partly based on misinterpretation of sensations or mental fear, was evident from the fact that he slept much of the day without the use of drugs.

(9)  General symptoms.

He was emaciated, notwithstanding the fact that he ate well, pointing to disturbance in metabolism. Sleep, he said, he never obtained, but fact was he slept more than eight hours a day. He often slept during the day and at night kept his nurse or daughter running to supply his numberless wants. It evidently afforded him relief to see everyone in the house suffer with him.

Since the onset he had been unable to perform continued constructive work. The smallest exertion exhausted him.

(10)  Preservation of the personality.

Those not in daily contact with him refused to believe that he was mentally deranged. There was no permanent memory defect. He was well oriented and his comprehension of affairs in general was remarkable.

(Case 27)

*Age at onset*: 57.

*Age at admission*: 60.

*Blood pressure* normal.

*Eye grounds* mildly sclerotic.

> *Symptoms*: Paroxysmal, severe pain in left elbow extending upwards. This pain, he said, was so intense he could scarcely bear it. He became emotional and would come home crying. At home he was irritable, suspicious, and depressed. Former labors he was unable to perform because of early and extreme fatigue.
>
> He visited some of the best clinics for a period of five years, but no positive diagnosis was made until he suffered an apoplectic stroke.
>
> Mentally, the personality was preserved. There was no permanent memory defect and loss of orientation.

(Case 28)

Mixture of Arteriosclerosis and Involutional
    Depression.

*Age at onset*: 50.

*Age at admission*: 51. (Menstruation had discontinued
    2 years before admission).

*Blood pressure* high.

*Physical symptoms* of arteriosclerosis present.

> *Symptoms*: Nervous, restless, resistive, sleepless, dizzy, irritable, complaintive, self-accusatory, fear of becoming insane, suspicious of relatives and nurses.
>
> *Delusional.*
>
> Said food was poisoned and would close up intestinal tract. She refused food and said if fed, "You are mur-

dering me." Said she would be thrown in a dungeon and then be eaten by mosquitoes.

*Personality well preserved.*

She at times talked rationally and comprehended the realities of life well except for her delusions.

These cases demonstrate the following:

(1) Slow and insidious onset of the disease.

(2) Difficulty in making an early diagnosis.

    (a) Objective neurological signs may not be present until late in the disease.

    (b) Subjective and mental symptoms are confusing, due to the fact that they are paroxysmal and influenced by emotional stress. (They simulate the neuroses.)

(3) Frequent preservation of the personality notwithstanding serious physical and psychic **symptoms.**

# CHAPTER XVII

## Senile Psychoses

A GRADUAL dementia may come on after 60, depending upon brain changes or disturbance of brain nourishment.

An early and general symptom is a memory loss for recent years, while the memory for early periods in life (5 to 15) is well retained. The memory of time is first disturbed. They forget their age and are unable to state the hour of the day or the day of the week. Next in order appears the inability to recognize place. They become lost in their own home and cannot find bath room or bed at night. When out for a walk, they become lost in the very vicinity in which they have lived for years. The last that fails to function correctly is the ability to recognize persons. They not only forget the names of their children, but mistake them for brothers and sisters and even for their own parents, long dead.

This memory defect is followed sooner or later by more serious signs of deterioration. Some of the senile sink into hopeless, agonizing depression; others become confused and slowly assume a stuporous attitude. Again others, although apparently still endowed with a perfect memory, have this memory filled with gaps of fabricated material. One of our patients daily told me of piles of gold out in the fields. For months she cleverly hid this story from the nurses.

The most problematic group is the one that suffers from expansive persecutory delusions. They become suspicious of the environment, neighbors and children are accused of stealing, and the mate of serious misconduct. They are often argumentative and boastful in society, and abusive and irritable towards members of their own household. The last two groups may also suffer from erotic tendencies, leading to foolish matrimonial ventures and sex offenses.

Reasons given by relatives and courts for the admission of senile patients:

(Case 29)

*Age*: 85

> Does not remember members of the family. He has ideas of wealth and authority. He runs from home and gets lost. He visits the neighbors, asking them to sing and play with him, and will not return home when requested.

(Case 30)

*Age*: 74

> He is very confused as to time of the day and the day of the week. At night he often talks for hours believing it to be day. He turns on the gas and forgets. He fires up the furnace when the temperature of the house is already too high. Notwithstanding his confusion, he wants to remodel the house, and tore down a porch of the house he rented to neighbors. If forced to desist, he becomes irritable and assaultive. At times he is anxious and fearful.

## (Case 31)

*Age*: 78

This man became depressed after the death of his wife. He was emotional, cried for hours, and said it was unbearable to live on. The last week he was fearful and restless, often walked the floor or streets both day and night. Said he saw the devil behind him with a flame of fire. Tries to hide from imagined enemies. Says he is lost forever and suggests self-destruction. He talks incessantly about his condition to whoever is willing to listen.

## (Case 32)

*Age*: 80

Was very irritable towards children. Forgetful the past two years. Gathers junk and hides it in the basement of his house [loss of the sense of values and property rights]. Has become indifferent as to his appearance. Threatened children and neighbors. Said he had thrown two policemen across the street. Boasted of immoral conduct and used vulgar language.

## (Case 33)

*Age*: 82

This patient had been confused, fearful, and disturbed for about two years. She was forgetful, restless, irritable, and destructive. Scissors and knives had to be hid as she would cut up clothing. She burned valuable garments and papers. At night she was often sleepless and kept the family awake by pounding upon the walls of her room. Medicine for sleep, as well as food, she at times refused believing them ot be poisoned. During the day she restlessly walked the floors, calling, "Mother, mother!"

## (Cases 34 and 35)

*Age*: 70

The following is the history of two successful business men, who, upon reaching the age of 70, developed paranoid delusions centering upon their relatively youthful wives.

The one maintained good insight into the realities of life, except for ideas of unfaithfulness in regard to his wife; the other had undergone extensive mental deterioration before he was brought to our attention, was hallucinated and strongly delusional.

The first presented a serious problem both to church and state authorities. His arguments seemed plausible, his evidence convincing. He presented his case cloaked in pious words, and his only purpose appeared to be to save his wife from perdition. It took him some two hours of fluent speech to present his intensely complicated story. This story not only included his wife, but also the preacher, elders, sheriffs, judge of probate, prosecuting attorney, and other important characters.

*Some essentials of his story*:

"We lived happily together for 7 years. At this time I noticed that my wife was paying unusual attention to a certain elder in our church. I reprimanded her for this misconduct. She denied everything. I next spoke to her repeatedly in regard to this matter, but she positively denied my accusations. 'There is absolutely no truth to it.' she would say.

"The way this matter was brought to my attention was as follows. I noticed that she would change in demeanor soon after we entered church. It further drew my attention that this occurred shortly after a certain family entered. She would then become restless and in general evidenced an inner tension.

"I know that a person's heart in the condition hers was would do exactly what I accused her of. I went to the pastor and elder, asking them to bring to her attention the sin of her licentious thoughts, but instead of settling the problem, they sided with her and accused me of being suspicious. They had an axe to grind with me, as I had also repeatedly warned them of not carrying out their duties as true shepherds of the flock. They sided with her, and from then on the struggle rested upon my shoulders alone."

His story was built up of fabricated material and ideas of reference. A glance, a shrug of the shoulders, a sigh, cough, or smile, all had secret meaning. The wife was not accused of immoral conduct, only of harboring lustful desires. He demanded that his wife should make a public confession of guilt, not for what she had done, but because of sinful, inner motives or thoughts.

The second man became no social problem as his mental disease was too evident. In the home, however, he was difficult to manage as he was at times irritable and aggressive.

He told me, "They have enticed my wife in a net. I call it white slavery. She has hired an attorney seven times worse than herself. My love for her turned to hate. Not one of my old friends stand by me. She disappears at night. She fights against the truth when I tell her the Scriptures. Her religion is devilish. She wants to run this house as a sporting house. She has doped me. God gives me visions, because of which I understand. I hired detectives, but no one helps me. There is no one I can trust."

The dreadful realization of isolation that may come over man at the dawn of senility, when his knowledge, no matter how wide, fails him and his senses no longer report true, is vividly portrayed in the last chapter of Ecclesiastes:

*Ecclesiastes* 12:1-8.

"Remember also thy Creator in the days of thy youth, before the evil days come, and the years draw nigh, when thou shalt say, I have no pleasure in them;

Before the sun, and the light, and the moon, and the stars, are darkened, and the clouds return after the rain;

In the day when the keepers of the house shall tremble, and the strong men shall bow themselves, and the grinders cease because they are few, and those that look out of the windows shall be darkened,

And the doors shall be shut in the street; when the sound of the grinding is low, and one shall rise up at the voice of a bird, and all the daughters of music shall be brought low;

Yea, they shall be afraid of that which is high, and terrors shall be in the way, and the almond tree shall blossom, and the grasshopper shall be a burden, and desire shall fail; because man goeth to his everlasting home, and the mourners go about the streets;

Before the silver cord is loosed, or the golden bowl is broken, or the pitcher is broken at the fountain, or the wheel broken at the cistern,

And the dust returneth to the earth as it was, and the spirit returneth unto God, who gave it.

# CHAPTER XVIII

# Diagnosis and Treatment of the Psychoses

TO DIAGNOSE mental disease we can draw on various sources, all of which aid in our final conclusions.

I. HISTORY.

A. *Family* history:

Was there mental disturbance in the family group? If there was, how numerous were the instances and what type of mental disturbance occurred? Not only the major functional psychoses are relevant here, as manic-depressive insanity, schizophrenia, etc., but also such conditions as epilepsy, feeble-mindedness, alcoholism, arteriosclerosis, senility, etc.

The search for evidence should not be limited to brothers, sisters, and parents, but must include at least two generations.

B. *Patient's* History:

1. *Past* history. Was the person while young well-balanced or unstable; shut-in or sociable;

sensitive or phlegmatic; serious or indifferent; changeable or persevering?

Was there a previous history of mental disturbance, and if so, what was its nature and did it permanently affect the personality?

2. *Present* history. Occasion, time, mode of onset and progress of disease to date. This includes any change in character, personality, relation to fellow-beings, etc.

II. APPEARANCE AND BEHAVIOR OF PATIENT.

A. *Appearance.*

a. Impression as to social attitude: fearful or bold; shy or aggressive; jovial or irritable.

B. *Behavior.*

Normal adjustment to reality; co-operative, considerate.

Abnormal reactions: negativistic, antagonistic, stereotype, stuporous, destructive.

III. MENTAL CONTENT. This includes disturbance of intellect, will, and emotion. It gives data on the question of orientation, obsessions, delusions, hallucination and amnesia; compulsion or inhibitory states; and emotional phenomena such as depression, elation, irritability, or indifference.

IV. PHYSICAL EXAMINATION.

A. *Neurological* examination. Any disease that destroys or in any way affects brain or nerve tissue almost invariably gives origin to outstanding bodily and mental symptoms. These may involve the sensory (senses) and motor (muscular) mechanisms or seriously involve higher psychical functions.

B. *Laboratory* examination. The blood, spinal fluid, as also the products of internal and external secretory glands may give important information in the differential diagnosis of the various forms of mental disease. By X-ray we can detect brain tumors, misplacement of brain tissues, and bone disease of the skull.

### DIFFERENTIAL DIAGNOSIS

As is the case with disease in general, so also in mental disturbance there are maladies that present similar symptoms and yet are fundamentally different.

Within the psychoses we must in the first place differentiate between the organic and functional forms. In organic cases (brain tumor, cerebral syphilis, etc.) there are positive brain lesions which either before or after death, may be observed by naked eye or microscope. In the functional conditions (schizophrenia, manic-depressive insanity, etc.) no such lesions have thus far been observed. The differentiation of these two conditions is important because of prognosis (hope for recovery) and treatment. In advanced cases the differential diagnosis is usually fairly easy as No. IV under diagnosis gives positive criteria. It is in acute cases, where the diagnosis is of most importance, that the differentiation is, however, often difficult, if not impossible.

Secondly, the major psychoses should be differentiated from the psychoneuroses and neuroses. These two conditions are rather frequently part of the mental picture in any disease. Its elimination is not only important to make a correct diagnosis, but also to verify the seriousness of the disease symptoms. In this case, as in the above, time will do much to make the differentiation clear. It is, however, of the utmost importance to study such cases from day to day in order to give the best advice and to follow out the most successful form of treatment.

Lastly, insane malingering, or the feigning of insanity, must be differentiated from the psychoses. This is scarcely ever of much import to psychiatrists, but needs consideration as it is frequently called to the attention of the public by the lay press in connection with peculiar conduct, delinquency, or criminal acts.

Contrary to common belief, it is practically impossible to imitate mental disease. Any qualified psychiatrist will soon recognize malingering. Only persons well acquainted with mental derangement have a chance to succeed as the following story demonstrates:

> There was some years ago, a Russian scholar in hiding in a German province. To prevent recognition and delivery to Russian authorities, he feigned mental disturbance. The psychiatrist, under whose care he was placed, found that the refugee answered all the symptoms of a certain type of mental disturbance but nevertheless presented something unusual. For this reason he had him watched and repeatedly questioned. All attempts to obtain a confession, however, failed. As a final resort he placed the patient before a large class of students, and boldly asserted that of all persons in his care who had feigned mental disturbance, this man was the most clever. He then explained to the class the refugee's methods and

reasons for his remarkable success; and thereupon made
it clear why the whole attempt was nevertheless futile
and childish play. The patient, believing that the psychiatrist had diagnosed his case and saw through his design, revealed his identity and confessed. (He had at
one time been an instructor in abnormal psychology.)

The reason why it is so difficult to imitate mental
disease is that the diagnoses do not rest upon a single
symptom but on a symptom complex derived from
various sources, as was indicated in the five headings
under diagnoses. It might be possible to simulate one
symptom rather convincingly, but it is impossible con-
sistently to carry out the full program.

It may be well asked, if the above is true, why then
the disagreement among psychiatrists when testifying
in courts of law? I am convinced that no such difference in testimony would exist, if the court and not the
involved parties would choose and pay the physicians,
and if these physicians were forced to compare notes
before the session of court.

## TREATMENT OF MENTAL DISEASE

In the organic psychoses, the treatment can be directed both against the disease proper and against the
symptoms this disease produces, but in the functional
conditions we can only direct our efforts against the
symptoms.

As the brain is a most delicate organ, and since what
is once destroyed in the nervous system is never restored, our hope of restoration after a destructive injury or disease is practically none. There is, however,
hope for recovery if brain tissue is injured but not de-

stroyed, as is found in inflammatory conditions, trauma due to accident, hemorrhages, brain tumors, etc.

The organic mental disease that responds to treatment most readily is general paralysis. This is a disease resulting from growth within the brain tissue of a bacterium, the spirochita pallida. This disease that has as its early mental manifestation symptoms of confusion and delinquency, and physically manifests sensory disturbance, degrees of paralysis and inco-ordination, is in its early stages favorably influenced by high temperature.

The high temperature, whether induced by a disease like malaria, or produced mechanically, has a very beneficial effect upon both mental and physical symptoms. Extreme confusion and memory defect clear up, delusions of grandeur disappear, while difficulty in gait is greatly improved. About 20% of patients suffering from this dreadful malady, after treatments, are enabled to resume their former duties in life, and some 40% more become much better able to adjust themselves to hospital routine. Before this treatment was instituted, practically all died of paralysis or convulsions within several years after the disease became evident.

The treatment of certain mental conditions resulting from endocrine unbalance has also produced interesting results. Children deficient in thyroid secretions may be greatly improved by feeding them thyroid extract obtained from animals. The dwarf-like, slow, stuporous, mentally underdeveloped cretin after a period of treatment begin to grow and develop physically, and besides greatly improves mentally. The thought processes become more active, intelligence rating rises, and social adjustment improves.

In brain tumor or organic brain injury, all symptoms may soon clear up if pressure is relieved and normal functioning again made possible. The last group of cases is (contrary to common belief) extremely small.

The mental condition caused by toxic factors due to diseases such as tuberculosis, and the acute infections, typhoid fever, scarlet fever, pneumonia, typhus, etc., all clear up readily when the disease has healed and the poisons have been eliminated from body tissue.

When the functional psychoses are concerned we face an even more difficult problem. Much work is at present done and millions of dollars are spent in the attempt to find the cause of these diseases, in order to be able more intelligently to advise prevention and to obtain recovery. This group, which increases yearly and includes about 70% of all mentally sick, naturally causes grave concern. Yearly new theories as to origin and method of treatment are introduced, but thus far little has been found that can be considered of importance. Could we reverse the hands of time some forty years, eliminate modern inventions and return the population to country life, much would be accomplished to stem the tide of mental collapse. Mankind has built a civilization which is reaching a momentum many are unable to carry. "Man is being destroyed by his own hand," as a certain author expressed it.

As to positive treatment of the major functional psychoses, the psychoanalytic school has tried in vain to obtain recovery by eliminating mental complexes, which were supposed to be at the root of the malady. Those believing that simple organic causes, like focal infection or toxic conditions, were at the root of the trouble, fared little better in their attempts.

Today the schizoid conditions are attacked by shock treatment. The early reports on this procedure were mostly favorable, but more recent reports are less convincing.

In the American Journal of Psychiatry, the report obtained from some one hundred physicians who had devoted full time to the shock therapy as given by Sakel, reported about as follows: "A wide diversity of views on the value of the treatment were expressed. One claimed better results in a series of controls than in the insulin series. The majority reported encouraging results."

The Journal of the American Medical Association, March 19, 1938, contains an abstract of an article by Querido and Van Der Spek on Schizophrenia after shock therapy, which reads in part: "In most patients inactivity and lack of initiative predominate. The essential schizophrenic symptoms have not disappeared. It is understandable that the psychiatrists at the clinic in the beginning are satisfied with the results of the shock therapy, for the majority of the schizophrenic symptoms, such as hallucinations, illusions, anxieties and motor unrest, disappear. The patient becomes apparently social. However, this improvement is only apparent; it is followed by a wavering attitude, lack of activity and lack of initiative, that is, the patient is not more social but merely more submissive; and particularly, the lack of those characteristics which in the beginning simulated cure lead to the disappointment of the optimistic expectations."

Dr. W. Overholser, Supt. of the St. Elizabeth Hospital, Washington, D.C., writing in the Journal of the Michigan State Medical Society, reservedly expresses a more hopeful view. He writes: "It is too early as yet to make any positive statement as to the ultimate value of the pharmacologic shock therapy. It deserves and is having a thorough trial, and there is every reason to feel conservatively optimistic."

After prevention, which is of greatest importance, the treatment of mental disease, whether organic or functional, is thus far, paresis and the above mentioned shock therapy excepted, mainly symptomatic and consists of prolonged rest, hydrotherapy, occupational therapy, and psychotherapy.

Of inestimable value in the treatment is an understanding, sympathetic, enthusiastic, and healthy nurses' staff, a staff that works not primarily for wages, but for the recovery of, or to afford humane care to the greatest of all sufferers.

Notwithstanding the seriousness of mental disease in general, hope for recovery, if the condition is of recent origin (six months or less) is favorable; and many even after a prolonged and serious mental derangement recover completely. Others recover sufficiently to make a good adjustment in home and society, and lead useful lives.

# CHAPTER XIX

# Mental Disturbance and Related Problems

THE above condensed description of some twenty forms of mental disturbance, demonstrates the tragic result of disease upon the highest faculties of man.

Physically, man, as it were, was the culmination of all forms created before him, and spiritually he made contact with a higher world. In body, mind, and spirit, he stood far above the rest of creation, but marred by sin, man forms the most helpless, pitiable, and tragic picture of all.

## MENTAL DISTURBANCE AND DISEASE

As to whether the body, the physical existence, or the *psyche,* is first involved in mental derangement is still a much debated problem. The gross materialistic conception of some 30 to 40 years ago has been forced to make way for a view that concentrates on psychogenic causes. The Freudian school, which to a great extent controls the field today, ascribes all abnormal mental conditions to intrapsychic conflicts and misuse of mental mechanisms. The last few years there appears to be a slow swinging back of the pendulum to physical or physiological theories.

My own view is that mental disturbance is due to disease of the body. By body I understand, however, infinitely more than a chaos of atoms. The body is a highly specialized organism and includes what is called life. Mental disease, therefore, in affecting the body may not only attack the physical substance but also the physiological functions.

But man is far more than matter and physiological activities. Man is endowed with spirit and is an image bearer of God. The last, namely man's spirit, is the essence of his personality, and gives man intrinsic value far above all creatures, and makes him an individual, responsible and immortal.

In what manner and in how far is this spirit of man affected in mental disease? It is my view that this spirit is not affected in a destructive sense. When we speak of sickness of the spirit we are using figurative language. The spirit's disease is of an ethical nature and concerns man's relation to God. The spirit or psyche requires perfect functioning organs, however, to obtain knowledge and understanding and to perform that most intricate function, rational self-expression. This is clearly illustrated when a fully developed person suffers from delirium due to acute disease or poisons. As soon as the disease clears up or the poisons are eliminated the mind again functions normally and the eye of the spirit sees and judges things in their true perspective. The recent shock treatment is also a most interesting proof that in the soma, or body, is the cause

for the strange mental symptoms found in our patients. Many of the stuporous, hallucinated, delusional,
schizoid patients soon after treatment regain insight
into reality. The mysterious voices that troubled him
are no longer heard. The dreadful visions fade away
as a mist, and the sense of smell, taste, etc., become
normal. The spirit was not diseased but certain bodily
organs functioned abnormally.

## MENTAL DISTURBANCE AND DEMON POSSESSION

It is my conviction that there is no relation between
mental disturbance proper and demon possession. Insanity or mental disturbance is a disease as all others,
and runs a rather regular, uniform course. Neither I
nor the nurses who work at our hospital ever found a
patient whose symptoms were of such a nature that
demon possession became our final diagnosis.

Demonism as the New Testament speaks of was evidently limited to that age of special miracles and is not
found today. Histories as related by Dr. Hugh White
(China) in his "Demonism Verified and Analyzed,"
are beyond doubt cases of major hysteria.

From a psychological viewpoint there is, however,
nothing unusual in a possession of man by spirits. We
find this illustrated in hypnotism, where the spirit of
one man takes possession of the functions of another
and to some degree controls them at will. Hypnotic influence, however, is only possible when there is a normally functioning body. It is impossible to hypnotize
an idiot, in whom for physical reasons mental functions
could not develop; and it becomes increasingly difficult

as insanity increases in degree. I believe for this reason that it would be impossible for the insane to be
fully demon possessed. This does not preclude the possibility, however, of the insane being influenced by
spirits, either good or evil. But such influence will
again depend upon the normality of the avenues of
approach and the integrity of mental functions; in
other words, upon the extent of mental disease. In
order to have demon possession in its most absolute
form, we need a healthy, normally functioning body.

## MENTAL DISTURBANCE, CRIME, AND DELINQUENCY

The fundamental difference between crime, delinquency and mental disturbance, I believe, rests in the
fact that mental disturbance is caused by disease, while
the other two have an ethical or moral basis. The fact
that the symptoms of both conditions may be limited
to misbehavior gives origin in early and obscure cases
to many difficulties in diagnosis. The onset of insanity
may be so insidious that it might be overlooked for
months in the very home of a psychiatrist.

The problem, why the mental patient evidences in
thought, speech and actions, besides the abnormal
which could be expected, so much that is morally
wrong, is a dreadful reality daily brought to our attention. The intelligence in mental disturbance is sick
and no longer a safe guide, but why should the out-
flow of thought so frequently tend toward evil? Pride,
jealousy, irritability, stubbornness, indolence, cursing,
assault, and even murder are frequently observed.

The only explanation is, God's conclusion in regard to man at the time of the flood, "For the imagination of man's heart is evil from his youth" (Gen. 8:21) ; or, as a certain modern philosopher exclaimed, "There is no crime so black, but what its roots are found in every human heart."

## Mental Disturbance and Suicide

Does suicide necessarily imply mental derangement? I believe not. If we see the numberless cases of suicide committed in countries like Japan and China simply to "maintain face," it is quite evident that the causes of suicide must be varied.

In all cases of suicide the question should, however, be considered, "Is there a possibility of mental disturbance in this case?" The answer to this question may be far from easy. The near relatives are often the only ones that can give important information.

Those who commit suicide because of mental disturbance I should classify as follows:

1. Those that find death in an accidental manner incident to a period of confusion. Such conditions of confusion are quite common in all forms of mental derangement and can come on rather suddenly. These patients may be run over by cars or trains, walk out of an open window, or from a precipice.

2. In many cases of acute mental derangement there is a period of extreme anxiety. Some impending doom seems to hang over the sufferer.

They themselves know of no cause, but the terror of this strange anguish allows them no rest. Fnally, to escape the resulting impossible existence, which to them appears endless in time and unbearable in degree, they commit suicide.

3. A third group commits the act influenced by hallucinations. The person may see an imagined fire and leap from a high building to escape destruction by flames. I recently saw a case of one who had jumped from a speeding train in order to avoid torture. Voices had been haunting him for hours telling him that he would be lynched at the next station.

4. Lastly, delusions, numberless in variety, may force the victim to seek recourse in self-destruction. A mother may destroy herself to save her children from imagined torture. A father demanded death because any increase in the length of his life would increase disgrace to his family. A young girl sought death because of the belief that her punishment would increase as her days increased, and since she was dammed anyway, the sooner she would end it all the better. (See cases 3, 4, 5, 6, and 7).

It is practically impossible to impart an idea of the power by which such sufferers are driven. I have watched them for weeks and months making every possible effort at self-destruction, and yet these same patients after recovery were happy and lived as before mental disturbance set in. The whole period of mental disturbance then appears to the patient as a dreadful nightmare.

If a person expresses suicidal content, it is our first duty to impress upon him that our lives are not our own and that suicide is murder. In order to prevent our becoming accomplices to such an act, it is further our duty to investigate the person's responsibility. If he is mentally sick, we from that hour share in the responsibility of his deed if we do not take the necessary precautions.

I am convinced that most mental patients who commit suicide are irresponsible. As it is impossible to determine the degree of responsibility in any given case, it is our duty to abstain from passing judgment on a person that has committed suicide in a state of mind that suggests mental derangement.

MENTAL DISTURBANCE AND RESPONSIBILITY

The witchcraft procedure of the seventeenth century presents one phase of this delicate subject, and the modern criminal who makes insanity an alibi, is the other. It concerns a very difficult problem, especially since it not only depends on a definition of terms, but to an even greater extent upon the world-and-life views of the psychiatrist and the judge.

The old definition, "An insane person is one who does not know the difference between right and wrong in relation to an act committed," is far too limited. This would include as irresponsible only the confused, delirious, amnesic and idiotic persons, and exclude the insane proper. Walter Lippmann this past summer suggested as a good guide in establishing irresponsibility, the question whether the person would commit the crime in the presence of others. (An irresponsible person, according to this theory, would never purposely seek opportunity to commit a criminal act in secret.) This suggestion evidently rests upon the same wrong conception of mental disturbance as the above. My experience is that mentally disturbed usually prefer to carry out their acts unobserved.

The promoters of both theories lack practical experience with and insight into the problems of mental disease. Diagnostic criteria here mentioned are far too simple to determine mental disturbance and irresponsibility. No single symptom is of positive value. A full examination as outlined by us under diagnosis (see index) must be made and the results carefully weighed before a decision of irresponsibility is reached. Obscure cases should, if at all possible, be hospitalized for at least a month and daily observed by an experienced psychiatrist.

In order to demonstrate our viewpoint, let us bring to your attention a few of the case histories mentioned in previous pages:

### Case No. 1 (p. 22)

The girl was institutionalized not because of mental disturbance, but because of irregularity in conduct. She was well aware of the fact that what she did was morally wrong and would, before the condition of mania set in, have been the last person to commit deeds such as stealing, falsifying checks, adultery, etc. What she suffered from was a driving force she could not resist. As soon as this manic condition subsided, she was grieved, ashamed, and felt deeply guilty before God and man for what she had done. It is my conviction that she was irresponsible.

## Case No. 2 (p. 24)

This case is of a similar nature, only more severe. For some three years he suffered periodically from a most intense disturbance. He cursed and raved and threatened to do bodily harm. This condition lasted until the disease cleared up. He then became a quiet, home loving, and honorable citizen — characteristics he had possessed before the disease set in.

## Case No. 5 (p. 30)

This case again presents a patient well aware of what she was doing. It was no sudden, impulsive act she committed, but one carefully planned. Neither the husband nor the relatives realized this patient's serious mental condition and the lack of insight of the prosecuting attorney is quite clear from the following: (This note was written in answer to my suggestion that she should be released on probation.)
"Dear Doctor:

"Although a statement of my reaction is unsolicited, I nevertheless wish to advise that I do not entertain a high opinion of a situation whereby medical testimony can be introduced of such a nature as to absolve a woman from criminal liability and bring about her commitment for medical attention, and, as soon as the hurdle of punishment has been overcome she is then no longer in need of treatment and should be permitted to go home. This may be good medicine, but sounds like poor law to me."

This letter I answered about as follows:

"Your letter I received and noted your advice on the case.

"I realize that it is often difficult for one profession to understand the viewpoint and conclusions of another, especially when they approach a problem from an entirely different aspect. I nevertheless wish to give you a few reasons why I came to the mentioned conclusion.

"Some years ago I admitted a relative of this patient. This relative on admission was disturbed and very delusional. There is therefore a question of heredity.

"The history of the patient, which I obtained from various sources, agreed in the following:

1.  She was depressed since the death of her mother several years before the onset.

2.  Contact with the sick relative greatly affected her.

3.  She had hallucinations of hearing, sight, and touch for over a year.

"According to her own testimony (which I take for granted) she had suicidal tendencies long before the attempt, and suffered severely of depressed delusions the last two weeks.

"Finally, shrewd planning and falsification, as done by her, does not rule out hallucinations and delusional content, but often accompanies them."

## Case No. 10 (p. 43)

This man, although somewhat peculiar, adjusted well in society. He held a gainful occupation and was loved by his family. A well-systematized delusion slowly gained control of his judgment, and the outcome was attempted murder. He was well aware of what he was doing. He carefully planned his deed, and was at one time confused or disoriented.

Reaching a diagnosis of a person's soundness or unsoundness of mind does not, however, solve the problem of irresponsibility in mental disease. A person may suffer from mental disease or defect and still be partly or entirely responsible. This is quite evident when we study the behavior and reaction toward legal or moral questions in the following:

(1) The Feebleminded (moron and imbecile)

The feebleminded's misbehavior cannot be judged by the standard of the normal, nevertheless we do not consider him entirely irresponsible.

(2) The Paranoiac and Paranoid condition.

These may, as case No. 10 demonstrates, harbor a single delusion and be irresponsible only as far as this delusion warps their judgment. Most individuals suffering from this condition are diligent in carrying out legal statutes or social and religious observances.

(3) Epilepsy with Mental Disease.

These cases are entirely irresponsible during the confused period, but become partly or entirely responsible as soon as the epileptic confusion subsides.

(4) The mental disease designated as the manic-depressed psychosis varies between entire responsibility and complete irresponsibility. It is in the transition period between these extremes that it is difficult for us to determine in just how far such a person shall be considered responsible.

(5) Among the schizoid conditions the katatonic brings up the most difficult question. In these there are at times sudden changes. One hour they may be open, pleasant and clear; while the next hour or day finds the patient confused and disturbed.

The fact that patients usually evidence self-control better in an institution than at home is another proof for the contention that mental patients are often not entirely and in all respects irresponsible. If the above were not true a mental hospital would be a bedlam and not a fairly well regulated institution.

Hoag and Williams in their book on "Crime, Abnormal Minds and the Law," write (p. 73) : "Sane people commit crimes, and insane people commit crimes, and it often happens that both are responsible for the crime committed. This fact greatly complicates the study of crime and criminals, of the sane and insane, and makes it necessary to determine not only the sanity or insanity of a criminal but the nature and extent of his insanity."

The fact complicates the question of irresponsibility. It should bring to the foreground the fact, however, that we focus too much upon the act when we consider this problem and not enough upon the future history of the person. Too many cases that commit crime in a condition of mental derangement are turned loose upon the public after being punished.

If a person is positively irresponsible at certain times or in certain respects because of mental disease, it is of the greatest importance that such a person is for the rest of his life protected against himself, and society is protected against him.

## NORMAL AND ABNORMAL DEPRESSION

The study of the paragraphs on mental depression brings up the question as to whether there is a difference between normal depression or despondency, and that arising on the basis of mental disease. I am convinced that in most cases of depression a positive answer can be given, if the person concerned is willing and able freely to discuss his symptoms and feelings. The difference between the two is not one of degree, but of kind. In all cases of depression that point to mental disease, we shall observe a strange certainty and an exaggeration of ideas. He is, for instance, not only a sinner but the personification of sin, sin itself, or the representation of the evil one, and all hope of redemption is absolutely passed. Compare with cases 3, 4, 6 and 13, the words of David in his Psalms of penitence, or those of Job in his despair. In our cases of mental depression, discussion of the problem is no longer possible. The mind seems to run in a vicious circle and thought is greatly inhibited. They repeat in almost identical words, day after day and month after month, their feelings of guilt and despair. Their reasons, why God punishes them thus, are often far-fetched or too irrelevant to allow consideration.

Further, we practically always find abnormal bodily sensations. As the patients themselves recognize these as peculiar, however, they may carefully hide them.

The fact that depression is based on mental disturbance should not change our methods of approach, except that we avoid all argument, make our assertions positive and our visits short. (This is a good rule to follow in nearly all cases of acute mental disease.)

## Marriage and Mental Disturbance

This brings up a personal and very serious problem in the life of many persons contemplating matrimony. The number of letters I receive asking for advice in this matter is rather large.

If the hereditary factors were well understood and offered no paradoxes, we could make this answer short, but the subject is obscure. On the one hand, it is true that a rather large number of mentally disturbed are found in certain families, but on the other hand it is also a fact that there is scarcely a family that has no isolated cases of either manic-depressive insanity, melancholia, schizophrenia, epilepsy, or feeble-mindedness among its members. If it is therefore hereditary, what course does this hereditary disease pursue: upon what is the possibility of transfer of characteristics based?

It is because of this uncertainty that I depend more on the personal equation of individuals, as far as giving my view is concerned, than upon strict hereditary factors.

My advice in general is about as follows:

1. Feeble-minded individuals or low-grade minds should not marry and bring forth children. (Children of parents who are mentally subnormal are very frequently mentally and physically abnormal).

2. Persons who have suffered from mental disturbance do better not to marry:

    (a) Because marriage increases responsibility.

    (b) Because in women a recurrence of mental disease is rather frequently associated with childbirth.

These individuals should be impressed with the fact that marriage, even though of inestimable value, is not essential in developing and leading a full-orbed life.

3. As far as persons are concerned whose father, mother, brother, or sister suffers from mental disease, here, as I said above, the personal equation should overbalance hereditary considerations.

Any person, who has reached the age of 22 to 25 years, has had no symptoms of mental disturbance and led a well-adjusted life in his home and society, has, I believe, prospects as favorable as the average. And as far as his children are concerned, especially if the mate is from good hereditary stock, these have as good a chance in life as the average child they meet in school or at play.

If, therefore, I am asked by a young man or woman as to what course to pursue when the question of marriage has arisen, with a person who has mentally disturbed among near blood relatives, I answer:

Obtain a personal history of the party involved. If this is normal and he or she has reached the age of 22 to 25 years, you can marry him or her about as safely as you could the average person you contact in society.

4. Where it concerns multiple cases of mental disturbance in both families, I believe it would be better not to consider matrimony, although also here the individual's mental health and stability is of great importance.

5. In this connection it is well to consider the marriage of cousins. I am convinced that first cousins should not marry, and that second cousins do better not to

marry. The question in these marriages is not primarily the blood relationship of the parties involved, but a duplication of abnormal characteristics. If there are no abnormalities in the chromosomes, blood relationship can have no detrimental effect upon the offspring. It is, however, impossible to determine in any given case whether a party is entirely free from abnormal or defective chromosomes. Besides outstanding abnormalities, as for instance, albinism or night blindness, there may be hidden characteristics that for generations have not come to the foreground. Such abnormal characteristics, due to multiplication of hereditary factors, may be brought out when relatives marry.

## Religion and Mental Disturbance

Among the psychoses, there is no such entity as religious insanity. No one ever becomes insane because of religious contemplation.

There are two outstanding reasons, however, why this is commonly believed. The first has its origin in the almost invariable religious mental content of the early psychotic, and the second results from the fact that the most rational and outspoken among the insane frequently consider themselves prophets or religious martyrs.

The cause of the exaggerated religious mental content of early cases of mental derangement may be ascribed to the dreadful anxiety or the horrible delusions and hallucinations by which such sufferers are often overwhelmed. When man feels reality giving way or displaced by a dreadful spectre, he naturally looks for shelter and protection, and flees to the throne of the Omnipotent.

The second reason for this conception has its origin in the mental content and reaction of the paranoid and paranoiac. In this type of mental disturbance, there are delusions of grandeur and persecution. This causes the sick mind to identify itself with what in man's estimation is the greatest, namely, God or God's representative on earth, — whether as prophet, priest, or king. And since the world not only refuses to recognize him, but opposes his plans and ridicules his ideas he concludes that he is a martyr. As these cases are mentally keen, outspoken, and argumentative, their number, although relatively small, attract much attention.

The fact that the mentally disturbed so frequently demonstrate a religious content merely proves that man is fundamentally religious.

We, as workers in a mental hospital, value in our patients a religious background. It gives more stability and inhibitory power to many sufferers, and affords us an important point of contact and guidance. Patients from Christian homes for this reason appreciate an environment or atmosphere in which the view of life is similar to the one they believed and loved before mental disturbance set in. It is true that long periods of suffering in certain types leave only a ray of the light man once possessed, but most of the early sufferers, and many chronic, remain mentally able to appreciate and find comfort in religion.

# Bibliography

*Manic-depressive Insanity and Paranoia*: Kraepelin (Munich).

*Dementia Praecox*: Kraepelin (Munich).

*Nervous and Mental Diseases*: Church-Peterson.

*Diseases of the Nervous System*: Jelliffe and White.

*Clinical Psychiatry*: Ebaugh-Strecker.

*Psychopathia Sexualis*: Kraft-Ebing.

*Crime, Abnormal Minds and the Law*: Hoag.

*The Doctor in Court*: Williams.

*The Criminal, the Judge and the Public*: Alexander and Staub.

*Foundations of Mental Health*: Bianchi.

*Mentally Defective Children*: Binet and Simon.

*Methods and Uses of Hypnosis and Self-Hypnosis*: Hollander.

*Arteriosclerosis: A Survey of the Problem;* Edited by Edmund V. Cowdry.

*The Structure and Meaning of Psychoanalysis*: Healy, Bronner and Bowers.

*Psycho-Pathology of Everyday Life*: Freud-Brill.

*Journal of American Medical Association.*

*The American Journal of Psychiatry.*

*Archives of Neurology and Psychiatry.*

# Index

★

*Retreat to Victory*

★

# Retreat to Victory

★

THE LIFE OF NATHANAEL GREENE

★

*by Clifford Lindsey Alderman*

CHILTON BOOK COMPANY
*Philadelphia   New York   London*

*For Peter Goonan*

# 1 ★★★★★★★★★★★★★★★★★★★

*A wise man is strong; yea, a man of
knowledge increaseth strength.* PROVERBS

Seated at the writing table in his quarters at West
Point, Major General Nathanael Greene had just finished
reading the letter from the commander in chief. The general
was a broad-shouldered, robust-looking man, handsome
in his blue coat with buff facings, a healthy glow in
his ruddy cheeks. The gaze of his blue-gray eyes, usually
so direct and keen, was clouded by the concern which had
also furrowed his high forehead. Now he understood why
General Washington had warned him that the command
at West Point might not be for long.

He took up the quill, dipped it, and prepared to write.
Then, thinking of what he was to say in this important letter,
he leaned back and looked through the window into
the distance.

The view was so beautiful that it wrenched his heart as
he thought of what might have been. Before him the hills
rimming the majestic Hudson River were aflame in all the
glory of this autumn day in 1780—scarlet, crimson, russet,
yellow. Beyond, the rounded summits of the mountains
edging the wild gorge of the Highlands gradually faded
into hazy blue in the far distance.

The general threw back his head, catching a whiff of
wood smoke that made his senses tingle. Then, with a
sigh, he began to write to his beloved wife:

3

"My dear Angel:

"What I have been dreading has come to pass. His Excellency General Washington, by order of the Congress, has appointed me to the command of the Southern Army."

He had hoped to remain at West Point for the winter. Kitty had planned to come. Accommodations for a lady would not be luxurious. The fortifications were little more than ruins, for the hope of stopping the British if they attacked lay chiefly in the immense iron chain, stretched across the river, that the general could see now from his window, and in the cannon mounted on Constitution Island, directly opposite. But Kitty had not minded the hardships of Valley Forge in the fearful winter of 1777–78.

As he wrote, the general told her how much he wished he might stay and be with her, but there was his duty.

The letter finished, he sat meditating over his new assignment. Command of an army of his own! For more than five years he had dreamed of it. Now that it had come, its taste was bitter.

This was a beaten and demoralized army he was to command. His predecessor, Horatio Gates, had thought to meet his British adversary, Lord Cornwallis, in full battle at Camden, South Carolina. The redcoats had given the Americans a terrible beating. Gates had lost at least 600 killed and 1000 captured—more than half his effective strength.

Nathanael Greene's job would be somehow to turn the remaining disheartened remnant into a fighting army again. With it he must keep Cornwallis from overrunning the South.

He knew well what would happen if he failed. There would be a great clamor for his scalp—from those of his

4

fellow officers who were jealous because he stood first in Washington's trust and esteem, from outraged members of the Continental Congress. His military career would be finished. But he would accept the challenge.

If anyone could accomplish the impossible in the South, it was Nathanael Greene. His whole life had been a struggle to gain his objectives. A host of difficulties and troubles had put gray in his hair early for his thirty-eight years. But he had faced them all squarely. He would face this greatest test the same way.

He thought back over those thirty-eight years. His first struggle had come in his boyhood—to overcome ignorance and make himself an educated, cultured man.

The general fell to musing over those early days, smiling to himself as he thought of his strict Quaker father. He could see him now on a night late in September. . . .

The great lopsided harvest moon hanging low in the western sky was a muddy orange-yellow as it neared its time of setting. Trudging homeward, Nathanael wondered just what time it was. Late, very late, he knew. Yet, though he had danced for hours, he did not feel tired.

The vast cavern of the barn where the husking had been held had been turned into a fairyland of soft light from candles in sconces hung on the walls. Their glow had made the pretty girls' eyes sparkle in the excitement and whirl of the country dances. Those fiddlers—they'd been given no rest at all from their scraping!

As for the husking itself, Nathanael had been one of the lucky boys. He had found a red ear while the corn was being shucked and had set out after the prettiest girl of all. She'd given him a merry chase, ducking and dodging, and then struggling, laughing, and squealing when he caught up with her and took his forfeit of a kiss.

5

Nathanael glowed when he thought of it. At the same time a small shiver wriggled up his spine. If his father knew of such goings-on. . . .

Why did the Quakers disapprove of dancing? His father, especially, being a Quaker preacher.

It didn't seem fair to Nathanael that he and his brothers should be strictly forbidden to attend such gatherings. Of course, the Puritans who had settled in Rhode Island frowned on them too, but there were plenty of people who didn't. Roger Williams, the founder of the colony, had made it a place where those of all religions could live in peace and worship as they pleased.

On that night in late September, Nathanael had gone early to bed with the others, as the Greene family always did. But not to sleep. He had waited until all was quiet in the farmhouse. At last he slid out of bed and drew on his good suit. Cautiously, lest the sound awaken his parents, he opened the window, let himself through it into the branches of a tree growing close beside the house, and reached the ground.

It was not the first time that Nathanael had sneaked out in this fashion. He didn't like to disobey his father, but huskings and dances were such fun. And he did like pretty girls.

His shoulders lifted in a shrug. If all went well he would soon be safe in bed, and his father none the wiser. Yet he did have a guilty feeling as he plodded along through the frosty night. Once, when his foot crushed a twig in the road and it broke with a snap, he gave a start that betrayed his tense nerves.

Now he could see the house looming up darkly in the moonlight, with its steep-pitched roof. *What was that in front of it?* Nathanael froze in his tracks. "Father!" he muttered softly.

There was no doubt of it. Nathanael could make out his father's familiar figure in its drab Quaker clothing, even the broad-brimmed hat the older man always wore. Mr. Greene was pacing up and down with an impatience that boded ill for Nathanael.

In an instant the young man slipped behind some bushes alongside the road. He crouched there, peering out intently. What he saw then seemed to make his insides melt into water. His father was carrying a horsewhip. Just above his head was the telltale open window through which the son had escaped.

Nathanael tried to marshal his scattered thoughts into some kind of order. Young as he was, he had learned to make the best of a situation, no matter how hopeless it seemed.

Suddenly he had it . . . lying flat, he crawled slowly toward the opposite side of the house from where his father stood. He hardly dared breathe, but at last the house was between him and the older man.

There, for some moments, Nathanael was very busy. At last he moved off, keeping the house between him and his father until he reached some underbrush. He made a wide circle through it and finally gained the road on which he had come from the husking. Then he strode straight for his father.

"Nathanael," came a stern voice, "where has thee been?"

Nathanael faced his father without flinching. He was a tall young fellow, nearly six feet, with broad shoulders and vigorous limbs, and a bearing as erect as a seasoned soldier's.

"I went to the husking, Father."

"A husking . . . was there no dancing?"

"There was dancing, Father."

7

"Thee knows that our faith forbids us to dance, and thee also disobeyed my own forbiddance. Therefore thee must be punished, though what thee feels will be as naught to what I suffer because I have a disobedient son."

"Yes, Father."

The elder Greene did not spare Nathanael. He sent the whip hissing through the air as he laid on a dozen lusty strokes. Nathanael did some more dancing, though it was not the sort prohibited by the Quakers. At each stroke he cried out, but if his father felt pity he did not allow it to interfere with his duty nor slacken the force of the lashes.

"Go now to thy bed," he told his son when he had finished, "and see that thee asks God's forgiveness for thy sin."

In his room, Nathanael undressed, removing a layer of shingles from under his shirt and breeches. Out there in the moonlight he had suddenly remembered the bundle of them on the ground on the other side of the house.

They had saved him pain, bruises, and welts, and while no one should approve this deception of his father, his resourcefulness was typical of Nathanael's later life. He had made the most of a critical situation; he would do so many times in the future.

Nathanael had been born there in the farmhouse in Warwick, Rhode Island, on July 27, 1742. His father, also named Nathanael Greene, had married again after his first wife died, leaving him with two sons, Benjamin and Thomas. Six more sons were born to him and his second wife. The oldest was Jacob, then came Nathanael, William, Elihu, Christopher, and Perry.

Warwick was a pleasant place for growing boys. The Greene house stood on a peninsula known as Potowomut, between two small rivers, not far from where they flowed into broad Narragansett Bay. It was close to one of these streams, known as Greene's River because ever since 1654 Greenes had lived there. It was a fine place for swimming, and from a little bridge nearby, the Greene boys used to fish for eels.

There was not much time for play, however. Almost as soon as they were able to toddle, all the eight Greene boys were given tasks to do. While their father was known as a minister, in the Quaker church this simply meant one gifted at talking who could lead the others at the yearly, quarterly, and monthly "meetings" which were the only services the Quakers held. Mr. Greene, like many other Quakers, was not only a shrewd, hard-working, prosperous business man, but a successful farmer as well. His sons were all trained to take part in these occupations.

From the time he was a baby, Nathanael grew accustomed to hearing the constant *clunk!* as the great trip hammer in his father's forge across the road on the river bank rose and fell with the turning of a mill wheel. Merchant-shipowners and captains of vessels in the seafaring colony of Rhode Island all knew of the Greene forge, for the anchors it turned out were famous.

There were other sounds that Nathanael grew to know well. Near the forge were a gristmill and a sawmill. Heavy carts rattled over the road with loads of corn to be ground. The great millstone whined as it turned, the hopper jarred as the grist was poured into it and was ground into meal, the sluice gurgled, and at times of flood the water roared as it spilled over the milldam. From the sawmill came the rip and screech of logs being cut into boards.

Nathanael took his part in all these activities. He could ply the huge bellows of the forge, making its fires leap

9

and pulse with life. As he grew older he was able to swing a heavy sledge hammer and use other tools of the black-smith's trade to shape hot iron, glowing cherry-red, on the anvils. At the sawmill he unloaded logs and piled and loaded lumber.

The farm was large and demanded constant attention. Farming is hard work, but the Greene boys made a game out of it. They vied with each other to see who could plow the straightest furrow, handle oxen to the best advantage, shape new-mown hay into the neatest stack. In the forge each tried to lift a heavier weight than his brother and shape iron into anchors with greater skill.

Nathanael was the strongest. His muscles developed quickly and became both tough and flexible. In Warwick he was famous for his feats of strength. Though he did not know it then, in building a strong and healthy body he was preparing himself for many hardships and rough living in the future.

Nathanael's mother died when he was only eleven, so the rearing of the boys after her death fell upon Mr. Greene. He brought them up strictly and made them work hard, but he was a kind and benevolent man at heart. In spite of his sharp business sense, however, he was narrow-minded in many ways.

There was no school in Warwick at that time, but schoolmasters often traveled about the countryside, hiring themselves out to instruct the children of families who could afford it. From time to time Mr. Greene engaged these men to teach his boys the "three R's"—reading, 'riting and 'rithmetic, or ciphering as it was often called. But once that was completed, their education was finished as far as he was concerned.

One winter afternoon when for once he did not have much to do, Nathanael set out for a ramble through the snowy countryside. His breath, coming rapidly as he swung along, turned to clouds of white mist in the bitter air, and his cheeks, nipped by the cold, were rosy. He walked with a slight limp because of a stiffness in one knee caused by a fall when he was younger, but it did not bother him at all.

Soon he overhauled another fellow of about his own age. As he came alongside he saw that he did not know the other young man, but he gave him a cheery greeting.

"Hello," said the stranger and held out his hand. "My name is William Giles."

Nathanael introduced himself. "Is thee from 'round here?" he asked.

"I'm from East Greenwich," Giles replied, "but I'm just home on vacation from Yale College in the Connecticut colony."

Nathanael looked at his new acquaintance with vast respect. "College?" he repeated. "Thee is at *college?*"

"Why, yes," said Giles. "Aren't you planning to go?"

Nathanael thought of how his father would explode at the very idea. "No," he said slowly, "I don't think so. I'm to go into business with my father in our forge." And he told Giles how his education had finished with the three R's.

"You should have more schooling than that," said Giles. "How are you going to amount to anything if you don't?"

Nathanael was intrigued by the thought, so new to him. As they trudged along, William Giles told him all about life at Yale College and his plans for the future. When they reached the neighboring settlement of East Greenwich, the two parted, but all the way home Nathanael could think of nothing but what Giles had said.

That night he said to Mr. Greene, "I'd like to have more schooling, Father."

The elder Greene's face reddened. "Schooling, indeed!" he blustered. "Thee has had all the schooling thee needs. Reading, writing, and ciphering are enough in our business."

"No, Father," said Nathanael quietly, "it is not enough for me. I . . . I want to amount to something."

The young man was determined, and his father, a just man, was finally convinced. "I cannot see what good will come of it," he declared, "but since thee wishes it, thee may go to Master Maxwell's school in East Greenwich."

The school was not college, but Nathanael was overjoyed. Adam Maxwell, a Scot, had acquired much learning in his native land before coming to America. And what Giles had said had opened a whole new world to the young man.

He had a devouring thirst for knowledge. Under Master Maxwell he learned Latin and geometry. He read the works of Horace and other Roman poets, of the philosopher and statesman Seneca, and the writings of Julius Caesar.

When Nathanael had completed his course of study, he was still not satisfied. If he were to continue to learn, he knew he must have books. But how to get them? He could expect no help from his father, who would consider money spent on books as thrown away.

Then he had an idea. Whenever he had a chance in the forge, he fashioned cast-off scraps of iron into miniature anchors and other toys. He stored them away until he had a sizable stock of them.

His father owned a sloop which was tied up at a dock on the river bank near the forge. Now and then the vessel would be loaded with ship's anchors and sailed across Narragansett Bay to Newport, the colony's largest town, on what was known as Rhode or Aquidneck Island. There the anchors were delivered to shipyards.

Nathanael often went along. When he was ready he took his toys on one of these trips. In Newport the proprietor of a general store saw they would have a ready sale and bought them all.

Nathanael headed straight for a bookshop. There he spent every penny of his new wealth on books. He simply could not get enough of them, and since his toys were eagerly bought, the store took all he could furnish. In time he had 250 volumes in his library, which was the wonder of a countryside where books were scarce.

With one of his brothers, the elder Mr. Greene owned another forge in nearby Coventry. In 1770 Nathanael was chosen to manage it. He moved to Coventry and built a fine house there which is still standing.

He was twenty-eight years old now, and prosperous. Shortly after coming to Coventry he was elected to the colony's governing body, the Rhode Island General Assembly. He had made many cultured friends and corresponded with them frequently. Books were his good friends too, and he continued to devour them. He still did not consider himself well educated. "I feel the mists of ignorance to surround me," he wrote in one of his letters.

He was still not married. One of his close friends was a brilliant young college graduate, Sam Ward, who had a pretty sister, Nancy. Nathanael fell in love with her, but she did not return his affection. However, since he was away from his father's disapproving eye, he often attended dances and other social affairs. He met charming girls, but not the right one.

Now the American Revolution was approaching. A military company called the Kentish Guards was formed in East Greenwich, Warwick, and Coventry to drill and prepare for the war if it came.

"Why don't you join us?" one of Nathanael's friends asked.

He thought for a moment. "I don't see how I can," he said slowly. "I'm a Quaker, and thee knows we don't believe in fighting."

"You wouldn't fight for your country if the war begins?"

Gravely, Nathanael considered the question. He knew how strongly his father would have disapproved, but the elder Greene had died a year or so before. Nathanael was a Quaker only because he had been brought up that way. He was intensely patriotic. If war did come he couldn't stay in Coventry and do nothing for his country.

"All right," he said, "I'll join."

"Good," said his friend. "It seems to me you'd make a fine officer. Can I put your name up for a lieutenant's commission?"

While all he knew about war had come from some books on military strategy he had bought, Nathanael was flattered and he agreed. When his name was suggested, however, one of the leaders of the new company laughed.

"What kind of an officer limps when he walks?" the man sneered. Nathanael was turned down. He was hurt and mortified, especially since the slight stiffness in his knee did not hinder him in sports or any other way. Nevertheless, he swallowed his pride and enlisted as a private.

He had no musket. Many men in Coventry did have guns they used for hunting, but they had either sold them to other members of the Kentish Guards or had enlisted themselves.

"I'll get one," said Nathanael. In the great town of Boston in Massachusetts Bay, muskets were surely to be had. He mounted a horse and set out on the 50-mile ride.

Boston was the biggest place he had ever seen. Within a few years after he came to Coventry, the American Revolution was approaching, and the city swarmed with red-coated British soldiers. Shortly before, Boston patriots had held the biggest "tea party" in history when they dumped the cargoes of three ships into the harbor rather than pay the tax Britain had imposed upon tea. To punish Boston, England had sent the soldiers to enforce military law in the town.

It was easy to see that the people hated them, especially the British officers. They were an arrogant lot who swaggered through the narrow, crooked streets, shouldering aside anyone who did not get out of their way. It was plain too that Boston was bristling and ready to fight. Muskets seemed as scarce as they were in Coventry.

At last, in a shop on Dock Square, Nathanael found a gun that would do. "I'll take it," he told the shopkeeper.

He was about to leave when the proprietor said, "Have a care the lobsters don't ketch ye with that musket. They'll take it away from ye."

Puzzled, Nathanael repeated, "Lobsters?"

"The redcoats. Some call 'em bloodybacks too."

Here was a new problem. A musket wasn't easy to hide. Looking through the shop door, Nathanael could see a large building just across the square. It was Faneuil Hall, whose lower story was used for a marketplace. A farmer who had brought a load of produce in that morning was driving away in his empty cart.

Nathanael darted after the vehicle. The farmer, busy with his driving, did not see him hide the musket under a pile of empty sacks in the back of the cart. Then Nathanael ran to where his horse was tied, mounted, and followed.

Boston stood on a peninsula jutting out into the harbor. The only way out of town was over the road which crossed narrow Boston Neck to Roxbury. Once safely on the mainland, Nathanael again overhauled the cart and managed to recover the gun without being observed.

15

Back in Coventry, he received a call from a delegation of Quakers. "We hear thee has joined the Kentish Guards," said their spokesman reproachfully. "Thee will be placed under the care of the meeting until thee makes satisfaction for thy conduct."

It meant that he must resign from the company and would be watched to make sure he attended no more drills. An important decision faced him. He must choose either to continue in his father's faith or leave it and remain in the Kentish Guards.

Nathanael respected the Quakers' belief that nothing could justify a war, but in his heart he was sure the patriots' cause was right and that if there was to be a war he must fight for that cause. He left the Quaker church and never returned to it.

If he was downcast because Nancy Ward had rejected him, something happened about this time that made him forget her very quickly. It probably occurred at the fine house of a distant relative, William Greene, in East Greenwich, where he was often a visitor.

That day William Greene had another guest, a niece by marriage who lived on Block Island, off the Rhode Island coast. At first sight Catherine Littlefield took Nathanael's breath away. He had never seen such a pretty girl. Kitty, as she was called, was not only beautiful, but she made his heart do somersaults with her vivacious ways and sparkling wit.

She was an outrageous flirt, who led Nathanael on cruelly. At one moment he would feel he had wings; the next, a dart from her flashing eyes would bring him tumbling out of the sky in despair. She did what no army in his long military career would be able to do—she captured him and he gladly surrendered.

Kitty was as fond of dancing, parties, and other social affairs as Nathanael. She did not have his love for learning, and hated school, but that didn't matter. He took her about and within a few months he wrote his friend Sam Ward on July 10, 1774: "On the 20th this instant I expect to be married to Miss Kitty Littlefield." And married they were.

They had less than a year to enjoy life together in Coventry. On the evening of April 19, 1775, one of Nathanael's comrades in the Kentish Guards galloped madly into the dooryard.

"Nathanael!" he shouted. "Have you heard the news? There's been a fight at Lexington and Concord in the Bay Colony! It means war! We're to march at dawn tomorrow."

By noon the next day the Kentish Guards were approaching the Rhode Island–Massachusetts Bay boundary, but before they could cross it a mounted courier overtook them. He bore orders to turn back, issued by the governor of Rhode Island, who was a Tory, loyal to the British.

The Rhode Island Assembly was not to be intimidated, however. Two days later it voted to raise a brigade of 1500 militia.

One of Nathanael's colleagues in the Assembly came to him. "We're choosing officers for the brigade," he said. "Your name is first on the list to command it as a brigadier general."

Nathanael was stunned. He, who had been denied a lieutenant's commission because of his limp, he who knew almost nothing about fighting a war, a *general?* He would have yielded the command to someone with more experience, but others who had been considered knew even less than he did. At last he accepted.

Nathanael Greene was probably the only officer in the American Revolution who rose from private to brigadier general in one mighty step.

2 ★ ★ ★ ★ ★ ★ ★ ★ ★ ★ ★ ★ ★ ★ ★ ★ ★ ★ ★

*Learn to labor and to wait.*
HENRY WADSWORTH LONGFELLOW

Now, at West Point, Nathanael's reverie of his boyhood and young manhood was interrupted as he took up his pen to write another letter. This one to General Washington:

"I shall prepare myself for the command as soon as I can. But as I have been five years and upwards in service, during which time I have paid no attention to the settlement of my domestic concerns, if it is possible I should be glad to spend a few days at home before setting out to the southward."

Five years. Years of all too frequent defeat and all too rare triumph, of want, hardship, bitter winters, times when even his stout heart had quailed and his indomitable confidence in final victory had been close to weakening. Indeed, even now, final victory seemed little nearer than it had in 1775.

Again Nathanael paused in his task as he thought of that year of 1775. His mind conjured up another scene from the past. . . .

Young Brigadier General Greene, at the head of his Rhode Island volunteers, was marching into Roxbury on the outskirts of Boston. The soldiers they met looked more like a gathering of tramps than fighting men. They were dirty and unkempt, and they slouched along the roadside. As Nathanael's brigade passed a tavern, two or three staggered out of its taproom, very drunk. Nathanael noticed also the motley collection of hovels they had built, some of old boards, others of turf and brush.

He hailed a man by the roadside who seemed to be an officer, since he wore a sword.

"I'm Brigadier General Greene from Rhode Island. Where's the army's headquarters?"

"Cambridge," was the reply. "Take the road that forks to the left at the crossroads down here a piece. Committee of Safety's headquarters 're 'longside the Common."

"Who's in command of the army?"

The officer shrugged. "I'm one of Old Put's officers from Connecticut. Hain't nobody tells *us* what to do 'cept him."

Nathanael knew he was speaking of Israel Putnam. Everybody in New England had heard of "Old Put," the fearless fighter who had distinguished himself in the French and Indian War by his boldness and heroism. But it seemed odd—an army without anyone in command.

There was a commander, however—General Artemus Ward. He assigned the Rhode Island brigade to an encampment at Jamaica Plain. Once Nathanael had his men settled there, he faced a discouraging situation. There was neither discipline nor order in the American army. It was by no mere chance that the Revolution had started in New England. Its people were the most fiercely independent and rebellious in all the colonies. Now the soldiers camped outside of Boston rebelled against military authority. No one was going to tell them what to do.

They obeyed orders only when they felt like it. If they tired of army life they went home without so much as a by-your-leave. They shirked the tasks assigned to them.

They stole money, food, clothing, and other valuables from their mates. Sutlers, the peddlers who attached themselves like leeches to the camp, sold them liquor, and there was constant drunkenness and disorder. The officers were not much better than the soldiers.

Nathanael's men soon became like the others. He called a council of his officers. In the tent which served as his headquarters he faced them, from colonels and lieutenant colonels down to the lowliest ensigns. Among them were his own brother, Major Christopher Greene, and his friend Sam Ward, a captain in one of the Rhode Island companies.

"I am going to have proper discipline in our camp," he told them. "As long as I command this brigade, orders will be obeyed."

"What's the use, Nathanael?" said one of the colonels. "You can't win this rebellion all by yourself. This is no army; it's a rabble. What chance does it stand against trained British Regulars?"

"None at all if we feel that way," replied Nathanael. "I believe we can win if we have obedience and order. These men may not be good soldiers now, but most of them have hunted all their lives and they're good shots. And they love liberty. Give them pride in themselves, train them, and they'll make excellent fighters."

He went on: "I want the men drilled every day. See that they keep their muskets clean and in good working order. They're to keep themselves and their clothes clean and neat too. A good many have drilled before in village train bands, but we'll give extra instruction to those who haven't."

He saw to it that his orders were obeyed to the letter. The Rhode Island camp was the neatest of the whole army, the men the trimmest, although like the rest they had no uniforms. Those who shirked or disobeyed orders were penalized with extra work. Sergeants and corporals were demoted to privates and more deserving men appointed in their stead. Captured deserters were marched before the paraded troops, triced up to a post, and whipped.

All this was infectious. Officers from adjoining camps came to jeer at Nathanael's efforts in the face of a hopeless struggle against Britain's seasoned veterans. They remained to ask this general who was as green in military experience as his name to help them establish order among their own men.

Meanwhile, the American army's objectives and strategy were becoming clear to Nathanael. The war had begun when a British detachment marched out of Boston to seize the patriots' stores of guns, ammunition, and provisions at Concord. After the skirmishes there and at Lexington, the Minute Men had chased the redcoats back to Boston.

Now the Americans were ranged in a long, sweeping arc around the landward side of the town. Their task was to keep General Thomas Gage's British army bottled up there. Thus the enemy might be starved into leaving by sea. Or, when the American army grew strong enough, it might attack and drive the British out.

The Americans were busy fortifying the hills along their line of defense. Nathanael and his men, like all the rest, worked night and day, throwing up earthworks and digging entrenchments.

Meanwhile, Nathanael met other ranking officers of the army. During his first council of war at General Ward's headquarters, he found himself sitting next to a fat young man with a florid complexion, who held out his hand.

"I'm Henry Knox," he said, and when Nathanael introduced himself: "Ah! I've been hearing about the good things you've been doing over at Jamaica Plain. Artillery's

21

my specialty. They tell me you're new to soldiering. Well, so am I. All I know about it came from some good friends —my books. Used to be a bookseller in Boston before the shooting started."

Nathanael's interest quickened. Here was a man who not only sold books, but appreciated them. This was the beginning of a lifelong friendship with Henry Knox, who was destined to be one of the ablest generals in the Revolution and later the first Secretary of War of the United States in President Washington's Cabinet.

Knox pointed out other officers at the council. Some would become Nathanael's close associates and battlefield companions in the years ahead. One was Major General Israel Putnam, a bluff, chunky, moon-faced man who didn't look his fifty-seven years. Another was Brigadier General John Sullivan, a tall, muscular, black-eyed lawyer from New Hampshire, quick-tempered, always arguing, inclined to be rash, but an able officer and fighting man.

The months of the siege were a time of hard work and long hours for Nathanael. "I go to bed late and rise early," he wrote to a friend in Rhode Island. In a letter to Kitty, he said, "I am feeling very much fatigued, having slept six hours in two nights."

Nathanael's success in training and putting his men under discipline did not make him conceited. He realized that other officers' experience of warfare was far greater than his own, for many had fought in the French and Indian War nearly twenty years before. He watched and listened, profiting by all he saw and heard.

He hoped for glory, but he was going to have to wait for that. On June 17, 1775, he was in Rhode Island for a few days when a courier rode in with the news that a battle had been raging that day on a hill above Charlestown, across the Charles River from Boston.

Instantly, Nathanael mounted his horse to gallop 50 miles through the night to Cambridge. He arrived the next morning, too late, though it is unlikely that he would have seen action in the battle of Bunker Hill if he had been there. The Rhode Island troops were held in reserve and did not get into the fight.

But he was elated over the battle, of which a London wit remarked, "We certainly are victorious, but if we have eight more such victories there will be nobody left to bring the news of them." Nathanael himself wrote to a friend, "I wish we could sell them another hill at the same price."

He never forgot the day of July 3, 1775, when General George Washington, who had arrived from Virginia, took over command of the army. At the ceremony under a great elm tree on Cambridge Common, Nathanael felt a sense of Washington's destiny as he looked upon him for the first time. To the father of his friend Sam Ward, he wrote, "Joy was visible in every countenance, and it seemed as if the spirit of conquest breathed through the whole army."

Washington was tall, graceful, elegant in an immaculate blue uniform with buff lapels and cuffs, wearing a sword. Nathanael saw a face that was less handsome than impressive, with its rather large Roman nose and blue eyes. This man, he knew instinctively, was not one with whom you could become over friendly. Yet he sensed that here was a great leader who would put his faith in those who deserved it. He resolved that if he could gain that trust he would not fail it.

Changes came quickly now. Many of Washington's actions were what Nathanael himself had wished for. The new commander in chief unified the troops under a single command known as the Continental Army. He enforced

23

more rigid discipline and order throughout the camp. Nathanael's respect and love for this great man increased daily.

He met others whose careers would be connected with his own. Benedict Arnold of Connecticut came into camp. Although he would later become the most notorious traitor in American history, he was a brilliant officer and bold fighting man.

Arnold soon marched, leading a force which was to penetrate the unknown wilderness of Maine into Canada. Outside of Quebec he was to meet Brigadier General Richard Montgomery, in command of an army coming from New York by way of the Hudson River, Lake Champlain, and the St. Lawrence. Together they were to assault the mighty British stronghold of Quebec.

With Arnold went Colonel Daniel Morgan and his corps of tall, rangy, fierce-looking riflemen, all crack shots, who had already marched more than 600 miles from Virginia. Morgan himself, a giant of a man, was the tallest and most ferocious-looking of them all. Nathanael would later have the aid of Morgan and his men at a time when he needed it desperately. With Arnold went Nathanael's brother Christopher and his friend Sam Ward.

As the year wore on, Washington was greatly worried about the army. For one thing, the enlistments of the Connecticut troops would expire on December 1. So would those of Nathanael's Rhode Island men on January 1, 1776. Unless they could be induced to re-enlist, nothing could stop them from going home.

Nathanael was indignant at the Connecticut men's lack of patriotism when they did leave. He made a speech to his own soldiers, strongly urging them to re-enlist, and was happy when a good many did.

He took other worries to heart as much as Washington

did. One was a critical shortage of the blankets, clothing, and firewood so necessary in the bitter New England winter. Nathanael wrote that many of his shivering men had to eat their scanty rations raw for want of fuel to cook them.

But his faith in final victory did not weaken. On December 20, he wrote to his brother Jacob in Rhode Island, "The calamities of war are very distressing, but slavery is dreadful. I have no reason to doubt the success of the colonies when I consider their union, strength and resources."

The Continental Army was short of arms and ammunition too—muskets, powder, shot, and cannon. What Washington feared most was that General Sir William Howe, who had replaced Gage in command of the British army in Boston, would find out how pitifully weak his forces were. If Howe struck before these shortages could be remedied, it would go hard with the Americans.

Nathanael's friend Henry Knox found a solution for the lack of cannon. In May, Ethan Allen and his wild band of Green Mountain Boys, from what is now Vermont, had done what no one thought possible. They had captured the supposedly impregnable British fortress of Ticonderoga on Lake Champlain, giving America its first important victory.

There were plenty of big cannon at Ticonderoga. Knox set out with a picked force of his artillerymen. They surmounted incredible difficulties and hardships to drag fifty-nine of the heavy guns on ox sleds more than a hundred miles across the mountains to Cambridge in the dead of winter.

Another stroke of luck came when an American privateer captured a British store ship. The vessel was loaded with 2000 muskets and bayonets, 100,000 of the flints used to fire these guns, 31 tons of musket balls and 30,000 cannon balls.

At last reinforcements were coming in from the colonies to the south, as well as more recruits from New England. Washington felt the army would soon be strong enough to meet the British. He proposed to force General Howe to action.

One hill, Dorchester Heights, on the extreme right of the American lines, had not been fortified because of the lack of cannon. Now, under cover of night, earthworks were thrown up and some of Ticonderoga's big guns dragged up and mounted there. They not only commanded the harbor, but could hurl cannon balls right into Boston.

The British general was surprised and dismayed when he saw what had happened. He could only order an assault on the new fortifications. Washington was ready for it. Two brigades were placed ready to counterattack by striking at Boston from the opposite side once Howe moved to cross the harbor against Dorchester Heights.

One of the brigades was Nathanael's. It seemed that his chance to show what he could do in action had come at last. His men were stationed along the Cambridge shore. A great flotilla of flat-bottomed bateaux, protected by huge floating batteries, was ready to ferry them across the Charles River.

That day, March 5, 1776, a great storm burst in wild fury over Boston. Rain swept in blinding sheets over the opposing armies. In such a deluge no musket, British or American, could be fired. The British fleet, which was to cover the redcoats' landing on the Dorchester shore with its guns, could not enter the harbor.

The storm continued all night and into the next day. By that time General Howe had changed his mind. A few days later his army embarked in transports and sailed away from Boston.

The siege was over and the Americans had won. But Nathanael Greene was still a general who had never been in a battle.

*There is the greatest practical benefit in making a few failures early in life.* THOMAS HENRY HUXLEY

In his quarters at West Point, disappointment clouded Nathanael's face as he tore open the seals and scanned General Washington's reply to his request that he be allowed to spend a few days in Rhode Island before starting for North Carolina:

"I wish circumstances could be made to correspond with your wishes, but your presence with your command as soon as possible is indispensable. I hope to see you without delay."

Nathanael summoned an aide. "My wife may already be on her way to join me here," he said. "Ride eastward toward Rhode Island. If you encounter her on the way, do all you can to hurry her along. I shall be leaving within a day or two."

It was quite possible, he knew, that Kitty might have set out for West Point. He had written her to come before he had received Washington's letter appointing him to command of the Southern Army. At best he could only hope to have a few hours with her, but it might be many months before he would see her again. Would she come in time . . . ?

Resolutely, Nathanael put Kitty out of his mind and turned to thoughts of what lay ahead for him. Uppermost in his mind was Washington's reliance upon him in this assignment which would test his ability, experience, determination, and courage as never before.

Seated there before his writing table, he clenched his fist. *He would not fail the commander in chief.*

Once he had failed Washington's trust. . . .

Although General Howe's army had sailed for Halifax, Nova Scotia, when the siege of Boston ended, Washington had information that it would soon return, this time to strike at New York City. Leaving a small force to garrison Boston, he moved his army to Manhattan Island.

Furious preparations were made to defend the city. Streets were barricaded and entrenchments dug. Nathanael was sent with Henry Knox to select the best positions for cannon.

During the months outside Boston he had gained something perhaps even more important than the battle experience he lacked—Washington's full trust and reliance. Toward the end of April, the commander in chief gave him proof of that confidence.

"I want you to take five regiments and go across the East River to the Long Island shore, General," he said, spreading out a map before Nathanael. "We must guard it in case the British land on the island, march westward, and attempt to cross from Brooklyn to Manhattan Island. At the same time the British fleet must be kept from going up the East River to protect such a landing from Brooklyn."

Washington's finger traced a curving path following the shore of the East River opposite Manhattan. "A chain of forts and breastworks will accomplish our design. If an attack comes in that quarter, you will command our forces there."

Nathanael was elated. "I shall do my best to carry out your orders properly, your Excellency," he said.

He and his men went to work at once—and none too soon. On the morning of June 29 he looked down the harbor and saw an armada of warships lying off Sandy Hook like so many hostile bulldogs, along with the transports which had brought Howe's army of 9000 from Halifax.

Washington's army was also about 9000 strong, but Howe landed his troops on Staten Island and waited until his brother, Admiral Richard Howe, arrived a fortnight later with over a hundred warships and transports. They brought nearly 10,000 more British soldiers and over a thousand German mercenaries—Hessians and men from the principality of Waldeck. Later two other fleets landed some 3000 more soldiers.

Nevertheless, Nathanael was confident when the defenses were completed. In his thoroughgoing way he made himself familiar with every inch of them, as well as the countryside beyond to the east. Out there was a ridge, excellent for defense against an oncoming enemy. Three roads cut through passes in it, but if these were patrolled there was a good chance that a British advance might be stopped there or at least delayed for some time.

While the Americans waited for the British to move, Nathanael was making his final preparations. Then . . . disaster.

On August 16 he was stricken with a raging fever. In a hospital in Manhattan he was so ill for two weeks that he nearly died.

On August 22 the British landed 15,000 troops at Gravesend Bay on Long Island. General Sullivan had succeeded to the command of the Americans on Long Island. By that time he had about 10,000 men, but he had had no chance to acquire the expert knowledge of the region that Nathanael had. Somehow one of the three roads that crossed the ridge was left unguarded. A British force slipped through. American troops sent to meet them were overwhelmed. Then the British main body advanced.

By noon on August 26 the battle of Long Island was over. The Americans lost about 300 killed and wounded, and about 1100 were captured. The rest only escaped when Washington hurried across to Brooklyn and got them safely back over the East River to Manhattan.

Nathanael was beginning to recover from his illness when he was told the news. He was beside himself with despair. "Gracious God! to be confined at such a time," he wrote in a letter dated August 30. "I have not the vanity to think the event would have been otherwise had I been there, yet I think I could have given the commanding general a great deal of necessary information."

Henry Knox did not agree with Nathanael's modesty. "Had he been there," he wrote to John Adams in the Continental Congress in Philadelphia, "matters would have worn a very different appearance at present."

In spite of the defeat, Nathanael's belief in eventual victory for America did not waver. About this time he wrote to a friend, "I apprehend the several retreats that have lately taken place begin to make you think that all is lost. Do not be frightened; our cause is not yet in a desperate state."

He had the fullest confidence in the men, though he did not think so well of the lower-ranking officers, except for his own. In his letter he added, "Our soldiers are as good as they ever were, and were the officers half as good as the men they would beat any army on the globe of equal numbers."

The defeat forced Washington to withdraw from New York City, which then occupied only lower Manhattan Island. He ordered fortifications built at the northern end of the island. The principal one was Fort Washington, near where today the majestic George Washington Bridge crosses the Hudson River to New Jersey. It stood on a rocky height, 300 feet above the river. Directly across, in New Jersey, a second strong point, Fort Lee, was built.

Washington then showed further proof of his trust in Nathanael by stationing his division at the two forts and giving him command of them, with headquarters at Fort Lee. Then the main body of the American army moved north to the mainland across the Harlem River from Manhattan.

Part of General Howe's army followed. After a battle at White Plains, the Americans were forced still farther north.

Howe then decided to go after Fort Washington. It was no great stronghold. Except for its location on the heights and the heavy cannon it mounted, an enemy might easily have stormed it.

Washington was doubtful that it could be held against the powerful British army. He called a council of war.

Most of his officers agreed with him, but Nathanael did not. He was now much more sure of himself and his ability to make his own decisions.

"I believe we can hold it, your Excellency," he said. "If we can do so we can keep the enemy's fleet from coming up the Hudson. It is important to prevent the British from reaching Albany."

It was important, Washington knew. General Montgomery's army had been beaten in its assault on Quebec and he had been killed. Now this northern American army was retreating up the St. Lawrence River. If its British enemy advanced into the New York colony in pursuit and Howe's army went up the Hudson and met them, the two could "cut off the head of the Revolution" by isolating New England from the rest of the colonies.

"I agree with General Greene," said Israel Putnam. So did Colonel Robert Magaw, in charge of the garrison at Fort Washington.

The commander in chief shook his head doubtfully. "Our position at Fort Washington is precarious," he said. "It will be better to evacuate it unless we can be sure the enemy's fleet can be kept from passing up the Hudson. However, since you are on the ground and can estimate the chances better, General Greene, I will leave it to your judgment."

On November 15, General Howe sent a flag of truce to Fort Washington demanding its surrender. Colonel Magaw wrote a reply in which he said, "Give me leave to assure your Excellency that, actuated by the most glorious cause mankind ever fought for, I am determined to defend this post to the last extremity."

Washington hurried to Fort Lee. The next morning Howe's army of about 8000 attacked Fort Washington. He had planned the assault well, for it came from three directions at once. To the east, 3000 redcoats struck across the Harlem River. On the south, Earl Percy advanced with 2000 British and Hessian troops. From the north came 3000 Hessians under General Wilhelm von Knyphausen.

Washington could have taken over command of the fort from Colonel Magaw, but he did not believe in interfering with a capable subordinate. From the top of the Palisades, rising almost straight up from the Hudson on the New Jersey shore, he watched the battle. Beside him stood Nathanael, Israel Putnam, and Brigadier General Hugh Mercer.

Nathanael's heart did a dizzy drop toward his boots as he saw the Hessians strike upward toward the craggy heights at the northern tip of Manhattan Island. Using a long glass, he could see some of them plainly.

At any other time he would have laughed. The Hessians looked like a procession of clowns. They wore great, top-heavy, brass-mounted, peaked helmets that resembled dunce caps, wigs powdered with flour and tallow, fierce black mustachios, ridiculous blue and yellow uniforms, and high black gaiters. No peddler on his rounds could have been so loaded down with equipment.

But there was nothing comical about their murderous-looking muskets, the bright steel of their fixed bayonets, or their ferocious aspects. Behind this column, led by some green-coated yagers or riflemen, other Hessians toiled at drag ropes attached to heavy field pieces and howitzers.

They met a deadly fusillade of fire from the Americans above. For a time they were obscured by blue smoke puffs that blossomed by the thousands from the entrenchments and redoubts up there, as well as from their own fire. Nathanael could see orange bursts of flame and smoke from the American cannon all along the defenses. The big guns' roar almost drowned out the rattle and crash of the musket volleys.

It seemed that the Hessian column could never surmount the cliff in the face of such devastating fire, but it inched up little by little. Then, to his dismay, Nathanael saw a second Hessian force making its way southward along the narrow strip of shore edging the Hudson. It too began an assault upward.

Time after time this second German column was driven back, but at last it surged up once more and the defenders' fire slackened. The officers on the Palisades could not know that many of the Americans found their musket barrels so hot they could no longer touch them, or that others' guns were so fouled from constant firing that they could not be reloaded.

34

The Hessian column, led by Colonel Johann Rall, scrambled and clawed itself over the top of the cliff and surged toward Fort Washington. General von Knyphausen's Hessians, who had taken the redoubt at the tip of the island, now came up. He sent an officer under a flag of truce to demand surrender.

Colonel Magaw knew his situation was hopeless. His men were exhausted. Their retreat was cut off in all directions. To the south, Percy's column was approaching. So were the two British columns which had crossed the Harlem River to the east.

Magaw surrendered. The British had won a tremendous victory. The 3000 men of the American force, save for about 50 who had been killed, were captured. If Howe struck swiftly, Washington's now badly weakened army was almost certainly doomed, and the Revolution lost.

Nathanael Greene, by his insistence that Fort Washington could be defended, had made the most serious blunder of his career, a mistake for which he must inevitably bear heavy responsibility.

# 4 ★ ★ ★ ★ ★ ★ ★ ★ ★ ★ ★ ★ ★ ★ ★ ★ ★ ★

*Strike whilst the iron is hot.* FRANÇOIS RABELAIS

Outside his window at West Point, Nathanael heard the slow *clip . . . clop* of hoofs as his big, handsome horse was led into the courtyard, saddled, and ready for the journey to North Carolina. He was writing a last letter to Kitty: "I am at this moment setting out for the southward . . . I have been almost distracted, I wanted to see you so much before I set out."

The officer he had sent eastward in the hope of meeting and hurrying her along had not found her. Then a rumor had reached Nathanael that she was approaching Fishkill, and he rode there himself, but it had proved false. The truth was that she had not yet left Rhode Island.

Having finished the letter, he folded, sealed, and handed it to an orderly with instructions to have it dispatched at once. Then he left his quarters for the last time, mounted and rode southward with his two aides.

He stopped briefly at the main American army's camp in New Jersey to receive final instructions. Washington assigned him one task which he did not relish.

"As you know, General Greene," the commander in chief said, "the information we have received regarding the Southern Army's defeat at Camden indicates that General Gates abandoned his command, fled from the battlefield and did not stop until he was nearly 200 miles away. Congress has ordered an investigation. You will hold an inquiry and send me a full report."

Gates . . . the one who had been jealous of Nathanael as Washington's favorite, and had tried to ruin his career. Here was an opportunity for revenge. But Nathanael had only compassion in his heart for the unfortunate man who had failed his country. . . .

When he set out again he had with him Baron Friedrich Wilhelm von Steuben, bound for Virginia, where he was to supervise the recruiting, training, and equipping of soldiers before sending them to North Carolina. It was good to have the ramrod-straight Prussian officer as his companion for the long ride. The fifty-year-old Steuben was a soldier after Nathanael's own heart. At Valley Forge, this veteran who had served under the famous Frederick the Great in Germany, had drilled and disciplined the raw recruits of Washington's army into first-class fighting men.

Moreover, he was a frank, simple man with a gracious manner and keen wit that endeared him to all. Like Nathanael, he was a scholar. One would have thought these two military men would have talked of little but warfare on their journey, but they whiled away many a mile discussing the Latin poets they had both read.

Now, as they rode south through New Jersey, the countryside brought back memories to Nathanael of the days after the capture of Fort Washington. . . .

That had been the most desperate time of his life. He had lived in an agony of remorse and apprehension. Foremost in his mind was the thought that he had failed the commander in chief. Did this tragic mistake mean the end of his military career? Would Washington put him in some unimportant post where he could never make another such blunder, where he could never hope to atone for it?

Preparing to evacuate Fort Lee before the British got there, Nathanael had written to Henry Knox, with Washington's main army: "I feel mad, vexed, sick and sorry—never did I need the consoling voice of a friend more than now."

Then came the headlong retreat across New Jersey, with General Charles Cornwallis and 6000 redcoats close on the army's heels. During that time Nathanael had found some consolation in his despondency. As a result of his advice to Washington to round up all possible boats on the Delaware River, the Americans crossed safely. All Cornwallis could do when he reached the river was to gaze across in frustration. Not a boat was to be had.

Washington's army was spread out for some distance along the west bank of the river opposite Trenton. Things had improved a little then. Reinforcements summoned from General Philip Schuyler's Northern Continental Army and the force Washington had left to guard the Hudson came in. The commander in chief decided to attack Trenton.

General Cornwallis had gone back to New York, leaving Major General James Grant in command of the British army, which was disposed at several points in New Jersey. At Trenton, across from the American camp, were about 1400 troops commanded by Colonel Rall—three regiments of Hessians, 50 yagers, 20 British dragoons, and an artillery company.

Christmas Eve came. That afternoon Nathanael received a message from one of Washington's aides: "His Excellency desires me to say that he will take supper with General Greene this evening."

When the commander in chief arrived at the comfortable, roomy stone house of the prosperous farmer with whom Nathanael lodged, everything was ready for the distinguished guest. In the room where a table had been set for them, a brisk fire crackled cheerfully on the hearth. Above it, on the stonework of the fireplace, was painted a rising sun.

Washington gazed at it curiously. "An unusual decoration, General," he remarked.

"I had it painted there to remind me of the birth of the American republic," Nathanael replied. He had been one of the first to advocate complete separation from England, and was overjoyed when the Continental Congress declared America a free and independent nation on July 4, 1776.

In these dark days when even Washington's confidence had waned, Nathanael Greene's had not. The rising sun showed his faith in victory.

At supper the commander in chief chatted amiably, though he revealed nothing of the reason for his visit. But when the meal was over he said, "I have asked some of the other officers to join us here for a council of war, General."

A war council meant action. Nathanael wondered anxiously what his part would be. A position of trust . . . or an insignificant post in the rear where he could make no wrong decisions?

Soon afterward the officers arrived. When all were seated about the table, Washington rose. "We have about 6000 men fit for fighting," he said, "but as you know, 2000 of the Maryland and Pennsylvania men's enlistments expire the first day of the new year. If a blow is struck, it must be now. It will be a desperate venture, but necessity will, nay must, justify the attack. I propose to cross the river and attack the Hessians at Trenton on the morning after Christmas. We will leave the camp tomorrow night and begin the assault at dawn."

General Mercer, who lived in eastern Pennsylvania, spoke up: "An excellent time, sir. Those fellows will be celebrating all day tomorrow. Christmas Day is their big holiday. I've seen it among the German settlers in this part of the country. Those Hessians will be in no shape for a fight the morning after."

Washington spread out a map of the countryside and the rest clustered around as he outlined the plan of attack. Then he turned to General Sullivan. "You will command the column marching by the river road, attacking the town from the west."

Nathanael's heart hammered furiously as he waited for the commander in chief to speak again.

"And you, General Greene, will command the second column, to approach by the Pennington road," Washington said.

Joy and relief surged over Nathanael. Washington still trusted him. His jaw set. This time he would not, *must* not, fail that trust.

Late on the afternoon of Christmas Day, drums beat long rolls, and Nathanael watched the 2400 soldiers fall into ranks, muster, and march off. Then he mounted and followed toward McKonkey's ferry, where the crossing was to be made. It was pitch dark when he arrived. Something cold lit on his nose and melted. It had begun to snow.

He peered out over the river. The current rushed past like a millrace. In the black water, immense cakes of ice ground against each other as they tumbled past.

Boats loaded with soldiers were already pushing off. There were no torches or lanterns which might betray what was afoot to sharp-eyed Tory spies on the other shore. Yet in spite of the darkness there was no disorder.

The only sounds were the low-voiced orders of the officers to their men.

Suddenly another voice pealed out like rolling thunder: "Push off, coxswain! Push off! All right, the rest of you fellows, embark in the next boat." It was Henry Knox, whose voice was as big as he was, superintending the embarkation.

Nathanael found his division and remained near while the men filed into the boats. The embarkation was slow work, especially the loading of 18 cannon and the nervous horses of the ranking officers. When eleven o'clock came, the better part of the army still waited on the west bank. Now the snow had changed to sleet. Whipped by a gale, it slashed viciously into the men's faces.

The commander in chief's figure loomed out of the darkness. "All going well with your division, General?" he asked Nathanael.

"Aye, your Excellency."

"Has the password been given you?"

"No, sir."

"It is, 'Victory or death.'"

Washington, Nathanael, Sullivan, and Knox were among those in the last boat to leave. It was listing to one side as they pushed off into the flood.

Washington, standing in the bow with his cloak wrapped close about him, called out, "Be so good as to shift your hindquarters to the other side of the boat, Colonel Knox." The oxlike artilleryman, who was in the stern, did so. The boat righted itself. Muffled laughter rippled among its passengers.

Safely on the New Jersey shore at last, the men fell into ranks. The word was passed along, "Absolute silence, on pain of death. Shield your muskets from the storm as best you can."

Nathanael's heart went out to the soldiers as his horse

picked its way over the treacherous footing of the road. He knew how pitifully thin and ragged their clothing was, how tattered their shoes, many bound with cloth to keep them from falling apart.

About halfway to Trenton, the column halted for breakfast. Some of the soldiers stood, some squatted as they ate the cold rations from their knapsacks. Others, too exhausted to eat, flung themselves on the ice-covered ground and were instantly asleep.

When the order came to resume the march, two men remained stretched on the ground. Two others, sent to rouse them, shook the motionless figures.

"It's no good, sir," one of them called out. "They're froze stiff."

The army plodded on. At a crossroads, Sullivan's division veered to the right onto the river road. Nathanael's, with Washington accompanying it, headed northward.

Dawn was only a grayness wrapped in the cloak of the storm, and the spires of Trenton's churches above its hundred-odd houses were invisible as the column approached. Then, from the Hessian outposts, came a popping of muskets, to which the American advance guard replied. The German sentries fled into Trenton, shouting, *Der Feind! Heraus!* (The enemy! Turn out!)" in guttural voices.

In the city, the rest of Colonel Rall's troops had celebrated Christmas Day long and lustily, far into the night. Now, in their billets, they lay asleep, stupefied by beer. Aroused, they threw on their clothes with fumbling fingers and lurched to their posts.

When the Americans reached the northern outskirts of the town, Nathanael's division split into two sections, according to plan. Two brigades charged straight south, down the two main thoroughfares, King and Queen streets. Nathanael himself, with the other two brigades, struck off to the left to swing in on the town from the east.

As his men plunged into the town, scenting victory, they had forgotten their cruel march. As for their leader, if the fear most men have on going into battle for the first time was in him, he did not know it. Nathanael felt only exhilaration and a boundless confidence.

Off to the right, cannon roared, telling him that Henry Knox had brought the army's heavy guns into position to rake King and Queen streets. From the distance, straight ahead, came scattered musket shots. That would be Sullivan's column, converging on the town from the river road to the west.

Nathanael heard music. Peering into the swirl of the snow, he saw a column of Hessians marching toward him to the music of their band. They made a brave show—the infantry in their blue uniforms; yagers in green and scarlet. At their head rode Colonel Rall, a chunky man, brandishing his sword and urging them on.

Both sides were firing, but Nathanael had a moment of alarm: his men's fire was scattering. In spite of their efforts, most of the muskets were wet.

"Fix bayonets!" Nathanael cried. "Charge them!"

The moonfaced Germans looked surprised, indignant, almost reproachful as the Americans swept forward. This was their kind of fighting, not Americans'. They did not like this approaching forest of steel.

Before the thrusts of the American bayonets, the Hessian line crumpled. "They run!" shouted Nathanael. "After them, boys!"

There seemed to be no escape for the Germans, for now Nathanael's other two brigades, striking south along the two main streets, wheeled to close in on Rall's force from the flank and rear.

The German commander was trying vainly to rally his

43

troops, bellowing at them. Suddenly he collapsed and slid off his horse. Some of his soldiers dragged him to the rear.

The Hessians were in a panic. Nathanael saw the color bearers of the two regiments lower their flags to the ground.

"Hold your fire!" he shouted. "Surround and take them prisoners!"

When this was done, Nathanael's brigades swung southward to converge on another Hessian regiment which Sullivan's division was engaging. It too surrendered. The battle of Trenton was over.

About 400 Hessians and British dragoons had managed to escape across Assunpink Creek, south of the city. Nevertheless, in an hour's fighting, the Hessians had lost 22 men killed and 848 taken prisoner, including 92 wounded. Brave Colonel Rall was dead.

Except for the two poor fellows who had frozen to death on the road, no American had died. Only four had been wounded. They included Colonel William Washington, a relative of the commander in chief, and young Lieutenant James Monroe, who would one day be President of the United States.

The night after the battle, the army went back across the Delaware. The exhausted men had a chance to catch up on their sleep. The next day, Washington ordered them served the best belated Christmas dinner the commissary could provide.

Just three days remained before the best troops, the Continental regiments, would go home. Washington pleaded personally with the men to re-enlist for six weeks more, appealing to their patriotism and also offering them a bounty of ten dollars. Where the money was to come from, he had no idea.

The soldiers were flushed with victory. Most of them agreed to remain for six weeks. Nathanael saw it as a providence. He wrote, "God Almighty inclined their hearts to listen to the proposal." In Philadelphia, the patriot Robert Morris managed to raise the money for the soldiers' extra pay.

In New York, General Howe was stunned at the news of Trenton. He sent Cornwallis hurrying back toward the Delaware with about 8000 men. Washington learned of it and dispatched a force to delay the British advance. Then he set the rest of the army to throwing up earthworks on the south bank of Assunpink Creek, just below Trenton.

The British came on steadily. On New Year's Day, 1777, they passed through Trenton and camped on the north bank of the creek after darkness had fallen.

In the American camp a gloomy war council was held. Even the optimistic Nathanael could not see how the Americans could stand against the superior British. "If we stay here we face ruin in the morning," he declared. He would have been more downcast if he could have heard what Cornwallis told his officers: "We've got Washington now. We'll go over and bag the old fox in the morning."

Washington favored fighting it out. Then Major General Arthur St. Clair stood up. "We can still avoid a battle and save the army. If we can sneak around Cornwallis's flank tonight we'll not only elude him but we can strike at his smaller reserve at Princeton. There's a new road to Princeton that runs through the woods and follows the course of the creek to the bridge at Quaker Meeting House."

The others, including Nathanael, were generally in agreement.

"Very well, gentlemen," said Washington. "We'll leave a few men to throw up new earthworks and be as noisy as possible about it. We'll have them keep the campfires blazing too."

A turmoil of activity began in the camp. Here and there a glow flared up behind the earthworks as the campfires were replenished. From across the Assunpink, the British sentries could hear the thud of spades. The sound drowned out the pounding of hoofs and rattle of wheels as the wagons, loaded with most of the American baggage, drove off to safety in Burlington. Meanwhile, the rest of Washington's army prepared for its hazardous escape.

At midnight the long column marched, stealing softly over the creek road to the enemy's left. It almost had to feel its way in the darkness over the rough road, which was little more than a trail through the forest. To the rear, Nathanael's horse stumbled several times over boulders. Henry Knox, just promoted to brigadier general, was having hard going with his artillery. The cannon, their wheels wrapped in cloth to muffle their rumble, often jammed fast between stumps on either side of the narrow way, and the cannoneers had to wrest them free with their handspikes.

It was two in the morning when the plodding, silent army reached Quaker Bridge over Stony Brook. The enemy was far behind, and Princeton only a few miles ahead. There the Americans would have the advantage both of numbers and surprise over the 1200 British troops.

Near the hamlet of Quaker Meeting House, the road forked. The way to the left made a junction not far beyond with the main road from Trenton to Princeton.

Washington galloped forward and gave Mercer an order: "Take the left fork with your division, General. At the main road, destroy the bridge there over Stony Brook. Then post your men to block any move by Lord Corn-

46

wallis toward Princeton, as well as any retreat by the British force there."

The rest of the army, headed by Sullivan's division, branched to the right over a second road, also leading to Princeton. Dawn came; then, all at once, the peace of the countryside was shattered by a distant rattle of musket fire. It came from the left, where Mercer's division had gone.

Washington signaled to Nathanael. "Take Hitchcock's brigade, Hand's riflemen, and Cadwalader's militia, and follow me." He spurred his big horse and galloped off.

Nathanael followed, confident of the men he led. He heard the blast of Mercer's cannon added to the rat-tat-tat of the muskets as his troops advanced across the fields on the run.

When they burst upon the scene of the fighting, Mercer's division was in headlong retreat. Beyond them, Nathanael saw a long, deployed line of scarlet. For the moment its advance had been halted by a hot fire from two American cannon off to the right.

Washington galloped up. "Follow me!" he shouted. "Hold your fire!"

Behind him, Nathanael and his force surged forward. Washington rode on, heedless of the enemy fire, until he was barely 30 yards from the redcoats. Then he reined up and ordered, "Halt!"

The soldiers did so, bringing up their muskets, but before Washington could give the command to fire, a British volley crackled and roared. The Americans returned it with a devastating blast.

Washington disappeared in a billowing cloud of blue smoke. Fearing he had been shot, Nathanael urged his mount forward. But just then the commander in chief's

47

voice came out of the cloud like a trumpet: "Bring up the troops! The day is ours!"

Mercer's men had rallied and were sweeping around one British flank; Hitchcock's the other. The enemy line wavered and disintegrated into a frenzied retreat.

Some of the Americans dashed for the bridge, which Mercer had had no chance to destroy. But the enemy commander, regaining control, led a bayonet charge which carried his force over it.

Washington bellowed an order at his cavalry: "After them!" The horsemen clattered over the bridge. Just behind them coursed the commander in chief with the rest of the army streaming after him.

He turned on his horse. "It's a fine fox chase, boys!" he cried, and spurred his mount to breakneck speed.

The chase continued for three miles. The Americans, close on the rear of the fleeing British, killed or wounded many and took 50 prisoners. At last Washington, knowing Cornwallis would have word of the fight and move toward him, ordered a halt. Then the troops marched for Princeton.

One British regiment had been left there. Sullivan's division had already made short work of it. After a brief, sharp fight, the British had fled. About 200 of them took refuge in Nassau Hall, the principal building of the college there which would later be Princeton University. One of Henry Knox's young artillery captains with a name that was to become famous, Alexander Hamilton, sent a couple of cannon balls crashing into the building's stone walls, and the redcoats inside surrendered. The battle of Princeton was over.

Nathanael was deeply saddened by the loss of a companion and able officer. During the British bayonet charge before Washington and Nathanael came up with their troops, General Mercer had been mortally wounded. Yet the Americans had lost only 40 killed and wounded against about 100 British, as well as some 200 taken prisoner.

Now Nathanael Greene was no longer a general with no more experience in battle than a boy who plays with tin soldiers. At both Trenton and Princeton he had lived up to Washington's expectations of him. That was what he had wanted most of all.

# 5 ★★★★★★★★★★★★★★★★★★★★

*Nobody ever heard of a quartermaster in history.* NATHANAEL GREENE

Philadelphia was familiar too as Nathanael rode into the city with his companions on his journey to North Carolina. During the winter of 1776–77, Washington had sent him there from the army's winter quarters at Morristown, New Jersey, to plead with Congress for men and supplies. Since that first visit, this largest city in America had been captured, held, then evacuated by the British, but it looked as busy and prosperous as ever.

Nathanael was almost deafened by the pounding of horses' hoofs and the clatter of wagons and drays over the cobblestones as they lumbered to and from the wharves where ships lay loading and discharging. Splendid coaches, chariots, and chaises carrying elegantly dressed ladies and gentlemen rolled past, the varnished spokes of their wheels flashing in the sun. More ladies thronged the immense market place, each with a servant to carry her market basket. Well-upholstered merchants strutted along in bright-colored coats and breeches of satin, velvet, and broadcloth, embroidered waistcoats and gold-laced, three-cornered hats.

The war seemed far away. Nathanael reflected rather sadly that Philadelphia seemed to care little about the sacrifices the men of the army were making.

Surely the people of this struggling new nation could afford to share some of their abundance with those who were fighting so that America could be free. Why didn't Congress see that they paid taxes to carry on the war? It had done nothing, and now, after five years of conflict, it could still depend only upon what each state was willing to contribute to the cause.

In Philadelphia, Nathanael conferred with members of Congress and officials of the government. He did his best to impress them with the need for more troops and equipment for the campaign in the South.

Just before he left, good news reached the city. In South Carolina, 1200 raw militiamen had met a force of 1000 trained Tories who were strongly entrenched on flat-topped King's Mountain. The Americans had routed them, killing and wounding over 300 and capturing all the rest. At least, Nathanael reflected, in this army he was to command there were some men who could fight.

More memories came to him as he resumed his ride. On the city's northern fringes lay Germantown; to the southwest, Brandywine Creek. At both places he had fought in savage, losing battles.

Brandywine . . . it might have been an American victory. General Howe had left himself open to a crippling blow. The British commander had divided his army, sending one portion in a wide circling march to get to the rear of the Americans. The other part might have been destroyed in the meantime if only Washington's intelligence had brought him positive word of the move. Instead, Howe had won, and then captured Philadelphia.

Germantown too had been a bitter disappointment. Nathanael thought of the night march toward the British camp there. The army had separated into four columns, each to follow a different road and strike from a different direction. As dawn approached, fog had swirled in over the countryside. Nathanael's division had been delayed for a precious half hour when a guide had lost his way.

But for the fog, too, one of his brigades would not have mistaken one of General Sullivan's for the foe and thrown it into confusion with a volley. And the fog, mixed with smoke from haystacks in the fields set afire by the British, had caused Sullivan's division to waste its ammunition on the wraithlike figures of the retreating enemy which loomed up and as quickly disappeared in the murk. Until then it had had victory in its grasp. With its powder and ball gone, it had to fall back, and the battle was lost.

Now, as he rode on, Nathanael's eyes veered westward in such an intent gaze that Steuben, trotting beside him, asked in his guttural voice, "Do you see something, General?"

"Aye," said Nathanael, "it is hidden by the hills, but I see it, nonetheless. I suppose it will haunt my dreams for the rest of my life. Valley Forge . . ."

"*Ach!*" cried Steuben, "I do not forget it, either!"

"The worst was over when you arrived, Baron."

"*Aber,* it was terrible—*eine Schrecklichkeit,* as we say in German. Poor fellows—I remember many who came to drill naked but for the blankets they used to cover themselves. Good men . . ."

"Aye, good men!" Nathanael echoed. "All they needed was someone like you to turn them into fighting men. When you got through with them they held their heads high and talked of what they were going to do to the enemy."

He fell silent, thinking of that winter of 1777–78 . . .

In each of the camp's motley clutter of little, drafty log huts, twelve soldiers huddled, shivering in their rags. Every day parties set out in search of fuel through country so plundered of trees, bushes, fence rails, anything that would burn, that it might have been swept by a forest fire. Behind them they dragged little carts they had built, leaving scarlet footprints on the snowy roads, for few had shoes with any soles in them.

Starvation and disease stalked the camp, specters as gaunt as the hungry men. Before spring came, 3000 soldiers and hundreds of horses died.

There was the day in February when Nathanael was at Washington's headquarters. A delegation of soldiers appeared and asked to see the commander in chief. Washington ordered them admitted.

The men stood before him respectfully, their hats in their hands. "Sir, the men in the camp are starving," their leader said. "It will be impossible for us to continue any longer unless we have some food."

Both generals knew all too well how true the words were. This was Washington's most desperate hour. He, and even the ever-optimistic Nathanael, were close now to losing all hope that the army could be held together until spring.

Washington turned to Nathanael: "General Greene, I want you to take a strong, armed party and make a thorough search of the country. Find whatever livestock, grain, and fodder you can and fetch them in. If necessary, you must take what is wanted by force."

Nathanael and his detachment set out. He divided it into small groups which spread out in all directions. At first they found little food. The countryside swarmed with Tories, who had hidden what they had not sold to the British.

One morning two men were brought before Nathanael. "We caught these fellows carrying provisions to the enemy," explained the officer who had captured them.

Nathanael had always recoiled from meting out the

brutal punishment of whipping, common in both the American and British armies. But as he reported to Washington, "Like Pharaoh, I hardened my heart and gave them a hundred lashes as an example." He hoped it would frighten others into yielding up food.

Perhaps it had. Gradually, the detachment rounded up horses, cattle, hogs, sheep, and badly needed wagons to carry them. The army was saved.

Not only Steuben's coming to Valley Forge inspired hope in the stricken camp, but another foreign officer who had joined the Americans late the previous summer was proving a tower of strength—a tall, hazel-eyed, handsome young man whose neatly powdered hair concealed its reddish color. Gilbert du Motier, Marquis de Lafayette, had come from France as a volunteer to fight for the cause. Congress had commissioned him a major general.

The many foreigners who had come to America and obtained high rank in the army were a touchy subject among Washington's officers. Indeed, it had gotten Nathanael in the bad graces of Congress. He and some others had successfully protested a proposal to appoint another Frenchman to command all the American artillery in place of Henry Knox. They had threatened to resign if it were carried out.

Thus Nathanael was prepared to dislike this latest interloper from France. He had forgotten for the moment how he himself had been made a brigadier general without a whit of military experience. Nor did he know that this serious-minded young nobleman was intensely devoted to men's liberties and America's cause. His dislike melted quickly before the charm and warm personality of the Frenchman. Lafayette became one of his greatest admirers. Not only were they to be future battlefield companions, but lifelong friends.

54

Something else had happened that winter which Nathanael would not forget either—the Conway Cabal. It had begun not long after electrifying news had reached Valley Forge concerning "Gentleman Johnny," as his redcoats called the colorful British general, John Burgoyne.

During the previous spring, Burgoyne had arrived at Quebec from England with an army of 8000 men. His plan was to strike southward up the St. Lawrence and Richelieu rivers, then Lake Champlain. Thus he might cut New England off from the rest of the American states and perhaps end the war.

Making his way southward after capturing the American-held fortress of Ticonderoga, Burgoyne had met the Northern Continental Army, commanded by General Horatio Gates. After a decisive battle at Saratoga, Burgoyne's entire army had surrendered. It was by far the greatest victory the Americans had won.

Not long afterward, a disturbing report reached Nathanael from York, where the Continental Congress had fled when the British captured Philadelphia. A friend there wrote him, "Various reports have been circulated through the country to prejudice the people against his Excellency and you, and that you are said to lead him in every measure, and that he wrote, if he fell, to have you appointed to command of the army." About the same time, he learned that these and other rumors against him came from Major General Thomas Mifflin.

Nathanael knew Mifflin was his enemy. This dignified, well-dressed man of about his own age, born a Quaker like himself, had first come to the army at Cambridge as one of Washington's aides. His agreeable manners had made him popular with his brother officers. But he did not return Nathanael's liking. Mifflin had been one of the loudest in criticizing him for the loss of Fort Washington.

Since then he had overlooked no opportunity to make other hostile remarks.

Washington had appointed Mifflin as quartermaster general. He had been an able one at first, but he had not been seen in the camp after the army came to Valley Forge. Meanwhile, the quartermaster's department had fallen into confusion, with supplies dwindling rapidly. Nathanael wondered if Mifflin had stayed away in the hope that the inefficiency would reflect upon Washington.

What was Mifflin up to, anyway? Nathanael soon learned what it was. Mifflin and Brigadier General Thomas Conway had hatched a plot to oust Washington and replace him with Horatio Gates.

Nathanael knew Conway as an unprincipled, conniving Irish adventurer who had joined the American army for all he could get out of it. In time his name was given to the plot. Conway and Mifflin had powerful friends in Congress who went along with the plan to replace Washington.

It was not so easy to understand why Horatio Gates was involved in the conspiracy. Gates had brought reinforcements from the Northern Continental Army to the camp across from Trenton before the battle there. Nathanael remembered him well—a kindly looking, well-built man whose graying hair and slight stoop made him look older than his forty-nine years. He had appeared to be a forthright fellow with no trace of sham or hypocrisy about him.

Although there were those who said Benedict Arnold and Daniel Morgan were the real heroes of Saratoga, Gates had won great fame and honor by the victory. The acclaim seemed to have gone to his head.

With the help of their friends in Congress, Mifflin and

Gates were appointed to the Board of War, giving them great power in all military matters. Soon Gates became its president. Thus the conspirators were able to press their plot against Washington.

Then Gates recommended Conway's appointment as inspector general of the army, and this was approved. Conway was also promoted to major general over more deserving brigadiers.

Nathanael was filled with loathing for the conspirators. In a letter to his brother Jacob, he wrote, "A horrid faction has been forming to ruin his Excellency and others. Ambition how boundless! Ingratitude how prevalent!"

He was helpless against them. Indeed, the Conway Cabal came close to succeeding. The plotters took advantage of Gates's victory at Saratoga to make Washington's failures at Brandywine and Germantown look far worse than they really were. In Congress, it was even proposed to have the commander in chief arrested.

Once he was convinced they really meant to destroy him, Washington was a dangerous foe to these enemies. The commander in chief saw to it that Congress was informed of certain scurrilous charges Conway had made about him in letters. Then Washington wrote Gates a scathing letter, showing that he knew exactly what was going on; a copy of this also went to Congress.

The conspirators were beaten. Fair-minded members of Congress were aroused. So was the public. The officers of his army were solidly behind Washington.

Gates wrote him a fawning letter of apology, denying he had had any part in the plot. It was never proved that he was actually a member of the Conway Cabal, but he seems to have known all about it and to have done nothing to stop it.

Mifflin resigned. Conway tried to bully Congress with a letter threatening resignation, but the members seized the opportunity to be rid of him and accepted it.

The Conway Cabal collapsed. Nathanael breathed more easily, for he knew that if Washington had been ousted, his own military career would have been ended too.

Meanwhile, a committee appointed by Congress had visited the camp. Nathanael talked with them and made a number of recommendations for badly needed improvements. Then, a few days after their return to York, Washington summoned him to headquarters and exploded a bombshell.

"General Greene," he said, "the committee of Congress, with my hearty approval, recommends your appointment as quartermaster general of the army in place of General Mifflin."

Nathanael was so stunned that for some moments he was unable to reply. Quartermaster general . . . the dull work of supplying the army. He thought of Germantown . . . how his division had lost its way in the fog and arrived late on the field. As he had done after the capture of Fort Washington, he wondered if the commander in chief had lost confidence in him.

At last he said, a little bitterly, "Your Excellency, there is a great difference between being raised to an office and descending to one, which is my case. There is also a great difference between serving where you have a fair prospect of honor and laurels, and where you have no prospect of either, let you discharge your duties ever so well. Nobody ever heard of a quartermaster in history."

"It is not always those who win glory who serve their country best," Washington replied. "At this time there is no more important task than the proper supplying of the army. I know of no officer under my command who is better fitted to carry it out."

When Nathanael, frowning and deep in thought, did not reply, Washington added, "I urge you, in the name of our personal friendship and the love of your country, to accept."

"I will think it over, your Excellency," Nathanael said at last.

Now, as never before, he wished he might have the counsel of his closest friend in the army. But Henry Knox was in Rhode Island with General Sullivan, looking into a plan to drive out the strong British force there.

In a letter to his friend, Nathanael told of his dilemma. "I hate the place," he wrote, "but hardly know what to do."

He could not wait for a reply. Actually, whether he realized it or not, there was never a doubt of what he would do. He was first of all a soldier, and as a soldier his duty was to carry out cheerfully and without question his superior's wishes.

He wrote the committee, accepting the appointment for one year. With his decision made, he plunged into his new duties with all the zeal, energy, and proficiency that marked everything he did.

★ ★ ★ ★ ★ ★ ★ ★ ★ ★ ★ ★ ★ ★ ★ ★ ★ ★ ★

*The prize of the general is . . . command.* JUSTICE OLIVER WENDELL HOLMES

Nathanael and his companions also stopped at Annapolis and Richmond on their way south. In the Maryland capital he conferred with Governor Thomas Lee; in Virginia's it was tall, red-haired Governor Thomas Jefferson. In both cities he appeared before the state legislatures. He had only one message for them: "Send me troops and supplies. I must have them."

At Richmond he parted with Steuben. Nathanael had great faith in him. If anyone could round up men and make fighters of them, it was the German baron.

Nathanael needed all the help he could get in obtaining enough soldiers to stand off the British army in the South under Cornwallis. Somehow too he must provide them with food and supplies.

Supplies . . . he was well fitted to cope with that problem. He had hated every moment of his time as quartermaster general, yet now it might prove to be one of the most valuable experiences of his career. As he rode toward North Carolina he thought of how he had striven to bring order out of the chaos Mifflin had left in the department.

"We must begin at once to build a chain of supply depots from the head of Chesapeake Bay through Pennsylvania and New Jersey to the Hudson for the storage of grain and hay," he told his assistant quartermasters general, John Cox and Charles Pettit, as soon as he took over his new duties there at Valley Forge. "Then the army will not run short of food wherever it is fighting."

"What about transportation when the army moves out of camp?" asked Cox. "The roads hereabouts are miserable."

"We will send out parties of soldiers to repair them."

"We are very short of wagons, General," said Pettit.

"While we are in this region we can use the Delaware and Schuylkill rivers for part of our transportation. We will build boats for that purpose."

Nathanael had another remedy in mind for the lack of wagons. Soon after taking office, he journeyed to Lancaster, where he appeared before the state legislature of Pennsylvania.

"The inhabitants refuse to give or sell wagons to us," he told them. "I want authority to seize them by force if necessary." They were not enthusiastic, but he so impressed them with the urgency of obtaining wagons that they agreed.

He found a solution for other problems. Hay for the horses was hard to transport because it was so bulky. He ordered big screw-compressors to condense it into small bales. He requisitioned tents so that the soldiers could be got out of the crowded, unsanitary huts in which they had lived all winter.

All these improvements cost money. To obtain it from the poverty-stricken government was Nathanael's greatest difficulty. He fairly bombarded Congress with appeals for cash, asking $150,000, but he was given only $50,000. So he went ahead and bought what was needed, anyway. He could only hope that the notes on the Treasury he persuaded suppliers to accept would be honored somehow.

Nathanael constantly had to prod these suppliers into furnishing the needed equipment, and to see that it was moved quickly to the camp. Within a few weeks, order had replaced confusion in the department; the chain of supply depots was established, and equipment and clothing were coming in.

Yet he was most unhappy. The worst was not knowing whether he would ever again take part in a battle, although Washington had mentioned rather vaguely that he might still have a command in action. Even the thrilling news that France had joined the war as America's ally could not bring him out of his black mood.

A powerful French fleet under Admiral d'Estaing was on its way to aid in the struggle. In Philadelphia, Sir Henry Clinton, who had replaced General Howe in command, received orders to evacuate the city lest the French armada bottle him up there with his 17,000 men.

Not daring to move by sea with his entire army, he crossed the Delaware into New Jersey with about 15,000 of the troops and marched toward New York. Washington's army followed. In spite of a heat wave that sent the thermometer soaring close to a hundred degrees, it outmarched the British. On June 27, when Clinton's sweating men were resting at Monmouth Courthouse, the Americans were only a few miles away.

Nathanael had been puzzled over Major General Charles Lee's behavior at Monmouth Courthouse. Lee had returned to the army after being a prisoner of war for over a year. The British were convinced he was the greatest of American generals and they did not want to let him go, but at last they had, in exchange for one of their generals who had been captured.

Washington thought well of this ugly, hawk-nosed

beanpole, whose clothes were not fit for a scarecrow and who always had several savage-looking dogs trailing at his heels. Nathanael also had respected him in spite of his arrogance and bad manners, for Lee too believed in strong discipline and constant training for soldiers.

Washington detached Lee in command of about half the army to attack the British at Monmouth Courthouse. The rest of the Americans followed the next morning in case their help should be needed.

Nathanael rode with Washington and his staff. They kept listening for firing ahead, but heard nothing.

Then, about noon, scattered shots reverberated in the distance as they were approaching Freehold Meetinghouse, about three miles from Monmouth Courthouse. Nathanael was perplexed. It didn't sound like a full-scale battle.

Washington too was unable to understand it. He spurred his horse to a gallop, followed by the others. Soon they met bands of soldiers fleeing toward them in disorder. They urged their horses to full speed. Crowds of retreating stragglers scattered as they thundered by, raising clouds of dust from the parched road.

Ahead, a group of mounted men loomed up. It was Lee and his staff, cantering toward them at a leisurely pace.

Nathanael had never seen Washington lose his temper completely, but now the commander in chief's voice trembled with rage as he reined up before Lee: "What, sir is the meaning of this? Whence come this disorder and confusion?"

Lee's reply was so confused that it made little sense, but Nathanael gathered that for some reason he had ordered his force to withdraw.

"Why, then, did you take the command if you did not

intend to carry out my orders?" Washington demanded. And not waiting for an answer, he gave Lee a tongue-lashing that left him cowering and speechless.

Washington spoke to Nathanael: "Take command of the right wing." This had been Lee's division until he was detached with the force which was to make the attack.

Nathanael, supremely happy because Washington's half-promise of a command in action had not been an empty one, led his division into the fight. The Americans, so well trained by Steuben, stood off attack after attack by the enemy. Nathanael's men hurled back a charge by redcoats under Cornwallis and drove them from the field. All along the American line, every division stood its ground.

It was so hot that Sunday afternoon that men on both sides died of sheer exhaustion, especially General von Knyphausen's Hessians with their great load of accouterments and heavy, brass-laden uniforms. Washington's splendid white horse died too, though no bullet struck him.

At five o'clock Clinton saw that he could not dislodge the Americans from their strong positions, and he withdrew his army. Washington, seeing a chance to annihilate him, wanted to counterattack, but his men, like the British, were too spent from the heat. That night the enemy stole away toward Sandy Hook, and by morning were too far away for pursuit.

General Lee was court-martialed and found guilty of disobeying orders and ordering an unnecessary and shameful retreat. He was sentenced to be suspended from his command for a year. Then he wrote an insolent letter to Congress, which dismissed him from the army.

Although this man had never been his friend, tolerant Nathanael could not find it in his heart to condemn Lee.

He called him an unfortunate man whose vanity and folly had brought ruin and disgrace upon him. It was not until years later that evidence was found indicating that while Lee was a prisoner of the British he had submitted to General Howe a plan to destroy Washington's army. Perhaps that explains his strange behavior on the field of Monmouth.

As for Nathanael, he soon had additional proof that Washington had meant what he said. It happened only a month after the Monmouth battle. General Sullivan was still in Rhode Island, but he did not have the strength to dislodge the 3000 British troops securely entrenched at Newport. Nathanael saw a chance to use the French fleet to advantage there.

"I urge you to send Admiral d'Estaing to Rhode Island, your Excellency," he told Washington. "The 4000 French marines he has aboard his ships can be landed to support General Sullivan. While the French fleet bombards the British entrenchments, we can easily drive them out."

"I have had the same thing in mind," Washington replied, "and I am sending General Lafayette with two brigades to reinforce General Sullivan."

Then Nathanael brought up something very close to his heart: "Your Excellency, I beg you to let me go to Rhode Island!"

Washington shook his head. "If you were to take part in the fighting you would have to replace General Sullivan in the command, since you are his senior among the major generals. It would not be fair to him."

"I will gladly serve as his junior in rank, your Excellency!"

A frown creased the commander in chief's forehead. "You must know, General Greene, that I not only depend upon you to keep this camp properly supplied, but I place much reliance upon your counsel in military matters. I need you here."

Nathanael's face fell, for he had let his hopes delude him into believing his superior would let him go. Kitty had been at the camp when the army was in winter quarters at Morristown, and also at Valley Forge, but he yearned to be with her again. He had only seen his son, George Washington Greene, as a tiny infant when he stopped briefly in Coventry in 1776 on his way from Cambridge to New York. He had never seen his new daughter, Martha Washington Greene, at all. Kitty, who had not been well, was expecting a third baby.

Washington, glancing at him, saw his keen disappointment. Suddenly a smile softened the commander in chief's grave expression, and he said, "However, in the dual capacity of quartermaster general and a military commander, you would be able to aid General Sullivan with the important problem of supply as well as on the field of battle. I will write him to create two divisions under his command, one to be led by General Lafayette and the other by yourself."

It seemed to the radiant Nathanael as he set off the next day that his horse's hoofs never touched the ground. He floated toward Rhode Island on wings of joy.

After a three-day journey he reached Coventry at sundown July 30 for a gladsome reunion with his beloved wife, whom he found recovered from her illness. Now he had his first chance to become acquainted with his children. Those of his brothers who were still at home flocked in the next day, along with a swarm of other relatives from the large Greene family in Rhode Island.

It seemed to Nathanael, after he and his division had joined General Sullivan, that victory was certain. Already, most of the enemy warships and transports at Newport had been destroyed by the French fleet, which was vastly superior to the British armada then approaching from New York.

But a terrible storm arose after D'Estaing put to sea with his mighty ships-of-the-line and frigates to meet the British. Both fleets were severely damaged. The British ships limped to New York for repairs. D'Estaing put back into Narragansett Bay, his vessels a welter of smashed masts and spars and tangled cordage. He announced he must obey the orders the French government had given him to refit at Boston in case any of his ships should be damaged.

Another blow then fell. General Sullivan issued a general order in which he made an insulting remark about how the French were deserting him. Nathanael and Lafayette tried to make amends, and pleaded with the outraged admiral to make repairs at a Rhode Island shipyard. Otherwise, they pointed out, the British might take advantage of the Americans' weakened situation, since Sullivan would no longer be able to depend upon the big guns of the French fleet to aid it with a bombardment.

Nathanael felt that but for the affront, D'Estaing would have changed his mind. He had great affection for Sullivan and thought highly of his ability, but he *was* rash at times. The French fleet sailed for Boston.

Then Brigadier General Sir George Pigot threw his army against Sullivan's. The American right wing, which Nathanael commanded, bore the brunt of the enemy assault. Twice his men threw the redcoats back. When they advanced a third time, he hurled his division upon them in a counterattack. "I had the pleasure to see them run in worse disorder than they did at the battle of Monmouth," he wrote to Washington afterwards.

But that very day a British squadron brought reinforcements from New York. The Americans were forced to give up their attempt to take Newport. Nathanael was bitterly disappointed. He was proud of the courage and fighting spirit his men had shown, but the campaign to liberate his home state had been a miserable failure.

When he rejoined Washington's army, two years of exhausting work, frustration, and many troubles began for him. In May, General Clinton embarked 6000 crack troops at New York and sailed up the Hudson to the Highlands. Fearing he planned to attack the American fortifications at West Point, Washington moved his army from Middlebrook, New Jersey, to a point on the Hudson a few miles below the British camp.

That summer, Brigadier General Anthony Wayne stormed and took the stronghold the British had built on the Hudson at Stony Point, killing and wounding about 150 and capturing over 600 of the enemy. Then General Sullivan, with about 2300 troops, set out on an expedition westward against the powerful Indian allies of the British, the Iroquois of the Mohawk Valley and the Finger Lakes region beyond. Sullivan laid waste to the country there, burning and plundering Indian villages as well as the farms of Tories.

For Nathanael there was endless work and no glory in all this. Without the horses, wagons, guns, ammunition, and a hundred other necessities he assembled and put into the field, these American triumphs could not have taken place. But no one so much as thought of giving credit to a quartermaster general for his part in the brilliant victory at Stony Point or the crushing of the Iroquois' power.

When cold weather came, Clinton retired to New York City. The American army went into winter quarters, once more at Morristown. It was a season of temperatures

68

below zero and of howling blizzards that buried the soldiers' huts in drifts. Although Nathanael strove desperately to keep supplies moving in, by early January starvation threatened the camp. At last food got through and the crisis was over.

Those two years did have their happy occasions, however. Kitty spent a good part of both winters with him. Most of the other generals' wives were there too, and there was much social activity. Nathanael was proud of the way his lovely young wife sparkled at these affairs.

Twice, in the early months of 1779, Washington sent him to Philadelphia. The second time, in April, he took Kitty with him. No doubt she had a better time than he did, for while both took part in the city's social whirl, he was having little better success than before in prying money out of Congress.

His family was growing. A second daughter, Cornelia Lott Greene, had been born while he was still with General Sullivan in Rhode Island. Soon after Kitty's arrival at the Morristown camp in 1779, another son, Nathanael Ray Greene, was born.

Nathanael yearned for the time when peace would come and he could settle down with his wife and children. But although the French alliance had improved the outlook for victory tremendously, there was as yet no end to the war in sight.

Nor could Nathanael see an end to the deadly treadmill of his existence as quartermaster general. He had been at it two years instead of the one he had agreed to serve. Now Congress was complaining about him.

Nothing made him so angry as to be criticized when he was doing his work well. Once during those troubled times the harassed Washington had lost his temper when he fancied his quartermaster general had neglected his duty. Nathanael promptly wrote a long and indignant letter of protest. By that time the commander in chief, well aware that he had no more devoted and efficient general, had regretted his outburst, and he sent a friendly and apologetic reply. Now Nathanael was even more bitter when some of his enemies in Congress charged that he was not only inefficient, but was getting rich.

It was a well-established custom that quartermasters general were allowed a commission of one per cent of all money spent for supplies. It was true also that Nathanael had received a substantial amount which he had invested in land, shipping, and other ventures. But in accepting the appointment, he had insisted that it be "without any additional pay, that I have as a major general." Nevertheless, the commission had been paid him.

From then on he refused to accept a penny of commission. Raging over such ingratitude, he wrote Congress, resigning his post. Washington, who was appalled at losing his valuable services, appealed to Congress, which took no action on the resignation.

Nevertheless, Nathanael persisted in his efforts. At last Congress accepted his second resignation, effective August 1, 1780, and Brigadier General Timothy Pickering succeeded him.

About that time, Washington left Nathanael in charge of the camp near Hackensack, New Jersey, while he journeyed to Hartford, Connecticut. There he was to discuss plans for action against the British with General de Rochambeau, in command of 6000 French troops who had arrived in America, and Admiral de Ternay, commander of the fleet which had brought them.

Shortly before Washington was expected to return, one of his aides rode into the camp.

"There's been treason at West Point, General!" he cried.

"Treason?" Nathanael repeated. "What do you mean?"

"It's Benedict Arnold, sir! He sold out to the enemy—agreed to turn West Point over to them!"

Nathanael stared at him. "*Arnold?* It *can't* be . . ."

But it was. Major John André, a British officer, wearing no uniform, had been captured as he rode south from West Point. Concealed in his boots were papers incriminating Arnold, in command at West Point, in a plot to deliver it to General Clinton for £20,000 and a general's commission in the British army.

Nathanael could not believe it. True, Arnold had been resentful—rightfully so—when Congress promoted less deserving officers ahead of him in spite of his brilliant record. Nathanael had heard the talk too of how Arnold had been overfriendly with Tories while he was military governor of Philadelphia after the British had left. While he was there he had married the daughter of a notorious Loyalist.

But *treason* . . . such a thing was unthinkable to a man like Nathanael Greene. *To sell out one's country* . . . it was beyond comprehension.

Washington had ridden with all speed to West Point, though too late to prevent the traitor's escape to the enemy. A few days later he returned to the camp.

"You will be president of the court-martial to try Major André," he told Nathanael.

The officers of the court-martial felt only pity for gallant young Major André, who had simply carried out the orders he had received from Clinton. But since the evidence was clear, and he had worn civilian clothing, making him a spy, the court could only declare him guilty. Nathanael, who had the repellent task of pronouncing the sentence, wept as he read the court's order dooming André to be hanged.

A few days later he went to Washington. "Your Excellency," he said, "the command at West Point is now vacant. I should be most grateful if it could be given to me."

For some moments Washington was plunged in thought. At last he said slowly, "I shall be happy to give you the command, General Greene . . . though I must warn you it may be only temporary . . ."

Later the delighted Nathanael had begun to wonder just what Washington had meant. It would be for a few months, probably—enough to let him rest a bit from his ordeal as quartermaster general. Kitty could be with him. The Hudson was magnificent in autumn. There would be no fighting during the winter months. Surely his command at West Point would last until spring . . .

It lasted less than three weeks. Then came what he had so long hoped for—command of an army of his own.

★ ★ ★ ★ ★ ★ ★ ★ ★ ★ ★ ★ ★ ★ ★ ★ ★ ★

*Trampled and beaten were they as the sand.* HENRY WADSWORTH LONGFELLOW

Soon after entering North Carolina, Nathanael and his companions reached Hillsboro, where a detachment of the Southern Army was camped. There too was an officer whose rare abilities as an engineer would be a bulwark of strength. He was Colonel Thaddeus Kosciusko, a Polish volunteer who had come to fight for the American cause.

Nathanael had immediate need of Kosciusko's abilities. After General Clinton had captured Charleston from the Americans in the spring of 1780, the British had overrun all of South Carolina. General Cornwallis was now in command there. His next move was expected to be against North Carolina. Nathanael had already studied maps of the country where much of the action was likely to take place. He knew the rivers of the region would be of crucial strategic importance.

At a council in Hillsboro he told Kosciusko, "I want you to ride ahead and survey the Catawba River from Mill Creek to Oliphant's Mill, Colonel. You will take particular note of all fords which may be used for crossings, and the possibility of using flatboats of shallow draft for transport on that part of the river."

Next he spoke to Brigadier General Edward Stevens, who commanded the Virginia militia at Hillsboro: "You will explore the upper waters of the Yadkin River in the same way, General."

Nathanael had been well impressed with the intelligence, energy, and industry shown by a young artillery officer who had joined his party at Richmond, Lieutenant Colonel Edward Carrington. He sent him on a similar mission to the Dan River, which closely followed the Virginia-North Carolina border.

Then Nathanael and the rest of his party rode on toward their destination of Charlotte, where the main body of the army was camped. He studied the country intently, his keen eyes missing nothing. The roads were rusty slashes through the wilderness, for this was red clay country, so common in the South. As they slogged along in rainy weather, through mud as slippery as grease and tenacious as glue, he saw that it would be hard going for an army on the march.

Part of the country was hilly, part plain. Much was primeval forest—mighty oaks, ash, maples, beech, hickory, and towering, arrow-straight pines.

They crossed three rivers and many smaller creeks. Here Nathanael was thinking of how an army might get over if there were no time to construct boats or bridges. Some of the streams were turgid, flowing slowly, but too deep in most places for wading. Others ran swiftly, betraying the nearness of the high mountains to the west. At high water they might sweep men and horses off their feet and drown them unless a shallow crossing could be found. At many points crossing would be all but impossible because of the extensive swamps edging the streams, matted with tangled brush, briars, and marsh grass, infested with deadly rattlesnakes and cottonmouth moccasins.

Another disturbing thing was the hostility Nathanael and his companions met in North Carolina. The region was a hotbed of Tories. Often, when the party stopped overnight in a settlement, there would be scowls, mutter-ings, and grudging service in taverns.

Some settlements were such nests of Loyalists that Nathanael remarked, "I feel as though we were in the enemy's own country rather than America." He knew what trouble the Tories could make for his army—refus-ing it aid, reporting its movements to the British, intimi-dating the patriots of the region.

At last, on December 2, 1780, Nathanael and his party rode into Charlotte. It was not a place to lift anyone's spirits, let alone those of a travel-weary general, appre-hensive of what he would find when he first saw the army he was to command. The town's clustered houses were stark and unlovely. Most were of logs lined with mud, with a single room and one window; some better ones were built of sawn and hewn logs with stone chimneys, or in a few cases of brick.

Nathanael was never one to flinch or dally in the face of an unpleasant task. He went at once to Gates's head-quarters.

The deposed general greeted his successor with great dignity and politeness, but Nathanael was aware of his apprehension. He realized what Gates, in this hour of humiliation, must expect from the man he had tried so often to discredit.

He immediately set about to put Gates at his ease. There was no mention of why he had come, of the campaign in which his former rival had failed so ignomin-iously, or of the investigation. The two chatted amiably for a few minutes of the days when they had served to-gether under Washington.

The anxiety in Gates's expression vanished. Nathanael had turned an ancient enemy into a friend who would remember him with gratitude and affection the rest of his life.

At last Gates said, "You will want to assume your new command as soon as possible, General Greene. I will have the army paraded tomorrow so that you can relieve me."

The ceremony was held the next day. Now Nathanael had his first look at the troops he must lead against Cornwallis. His expectations had not been high, but what he saw appalled him.

This was his *army*—this motley, gaunt and hungry-eyed herd of tatterdemalions? Some wore the farmer's rough homespun, some the buckskins of the mountaineer and woodsman, with moccasins on their feet and coonskin caps on their heads. All were ragged and some all but naked. They slouched when they walked, and they looked like what they were—beaten men.

Nathanael felt somewhat better after he had seen and talked with the army's ranking officers. They seemed to know what they were doing. A number had fought at Camden and were itching for a chance to avenge that inglorious defeat.

Nathanael's attention was drawn particularly to Major General Isaac Huger, an unassuming man of about his own age. He felt an instinctive confidence in this South Carolinian who had fought all through the war in the South.

"What is the present strength of the army?" he asked Huger.

"About 2300 men, General."

Nathanael looked surprised. "Is it possible there were 2300 men assembled when I assumed command?"

"No, General," replied Huger. "We have only about 800 here who are fit for duty. The rest are either sick, weakened by hunger, or so ill-clad they cannot possibly fight.

However, there is a scouting force of about 600 excellent troops under General Morgan in the field."

"How many of the men are Continentals?"

"About half, sir."

"I notice the men are living in miserable huts. Are there no tents?"

Huger spread his hands in a despairing gesture. "General, we have no tents, no proper clothing, few arms or ammunition of any kind. There are no wagons to transport these supplies, even if we could obtain them. And the men are starving."

"What of our partisan forces which are aiding the cause here in the South?"

"Generals Marion and Pickens are in South Carolina. Marion lies in hiding on the Black River, whence he harasses the enemy post at Georgetown. Pickens is in the west, collecting recruits and threatening the British outpost at Ninety-Six."

"And General Sumter?"

"Out of action for the time, unfortunately. He was wounded when he beat the Green Dragoon in a fight in South Carolina. But the Gamecock'll be back—" Huger stopped, then said, "I beg your pardon, sir—mayhap you've not heard what the men call General Sumter. The Green Dragoon's the enemy leader, Tarleton."

Nathanael smiled. "Aye, General Huger, I know."

He was thoroughly familiar with Brigadier General Thomas Sumter's nickname, as well as that of Brigadier General Francis Marion, whom the British called the Swamp Fox. Familiar too with the spectacular deeds of these leaders of volunteer bands which had long made life miserable for the enemy in the South with their daring raids on outposts and scouting parties. He hoped soon to meet them all.

Nor was the name "Green Dragoon" strange to him. He knew all about Lieutenant Colonel Sir Banastre Tarleton, commander of a marauding band of green-coated British cavalry. Tarleton's cold-blooded butchery of prisoners who surrendered had made his name dreaded by many an American soldier.

"You'll not lack for prompt and reliable intelligence from our partisans, General Greene," Huger went on. "They know every move the British make."

Nathanael nodded in satisfaction. He turned to the others at the council he had called.

"Gentlemen, our situation is precarious, but not desperate, I think," he said. "I expect reinforcements from the north soon. As for the supplies and equipment we so sorely need, I have already asked for them. I shall take further steps at once to make sure they are not delayed. And with your help, it is my design to turn these men of ours into a fighting army. Our purpose is to end Lord Cornwallis's mastery of the South. I promise you that I shall not rest until it is accomplished."

Nathanael worked like a plow horse to carry out his promises. When Lieutenant Colonel Carrington reached the camp after his survey of the Dan River, Nathanael summoned him to headquarters.

"The army urgently needs a dependable quartermaster," he said. "I believe you are the man for the post. Will you take it?" And when Carrington agreed: "I am arranging for supplies to be obtained in Virginia. You will ride at once to Richmond, collect them and keep them moving to us."

He had his eye on another able officer for the equally important post of commissary general. Young Colonel William Davie looked dismayed when he was asked to accept the appointment. Nathanael, thinking of his own

78

feelings when Washington had asked him to be quarter-master general, was not surprised. Like himself, Davie was first of all a fighting man. But like Nathanael too, he was a soldier, and he agreed to serve.

Nathanael then set about to see that the supplies and food Carrington and Davie must have would be available. He wrote to the North Carolina Board of War, saying that depots stocked with provisions to last for a month must be set up at several points to provide for an army on the march. Three thousand cattle must also be collected at various locations where they could be slaughtered for food and shoe leather. Nathanael told the board bluntly that if these things were not done, both North and South Carolina must be abandoned to the British.

He ordered lead from a mine in Virginia shipped to Salem, North Carolina. There artisans of the Moravian religious sect had offered to turn it into musket balls. From an iron works in Virginia, he requisitioned camp kettles and iron bars which would be fashioned into horseshoes by blacksmiths loyal to the American cause. He managed to obtain a supply of denim and sheeting which the patriotic women of Salisbury made into breeches and shirts. And he ordered Kosciusko to have flatboats built which could be transported on wagons as the army moved.

Nathanael's efforts were obstructed by a mountain of difficulties. He got little rest. He would sit late into the night before his writing table, issuing orders and scratching off letters with a busy quill.

Nearer at hand was the problem of his men. He soon found that the militia in the South were even less dependable than those of Washington's army. They constantly wandered off, went home and returned only if they felt like it. The Continental troops were different. They were enlisted either for the duration of the war or for a long period. Thus they could be trained, disciplined, and obtain more experience in battle.

"Desertions must be stopped," Nathanael told his officers. "I shall make an example of the next deserter."

A few days later one was apprehended, tried by court-martial, and sentenced to death. The entire army was paraded to see the offender hanged. The desertions stopped.

Meanwhile, there was the investigation of General Gates's conduct to be faced. Washington had given Nathanael written instructions to consult with his officers as to what should be done. "If they think it cannot take place immediately," the orders said, "you will inform Major General Gates of it, and transmit to me their decision."

To his intense relief, Nathanael found that few of the witnesses whose testimony would be important were at the camp. His officers agreed that a proper investigation was impossible at that time.

Gates's response was courageous when Nathanael informed him. "I would prefer to face it now, General Greene," he said in his dignified way, "but if that is the decision, I will abide by it."

Then he departed for his home in Virginia to await action in his case. In his report to Washington, Nathanael said that in his opinion neither the army nor the country would benefit by heaping any more disgrace upon the unhappy general. No inquiry was ever held.

Now Nathanael began to think of his campaign against Cornwallis. One thing was certain: the army must move from Charlotte. Whatever food it obtained had to come from a distance, for in October Cornwallis had plundered the surrounding region.

Nathanael sent Kosciusko to explore the country along

the Pee Dee River in South Carolina for a new site. Then he called Daniel Morgan and his advance force back to Charlotte. It had been more than four years since he had seen the tall, fierce-looking Old Wagoner, who had gained his nickname driving wagons in General Braddock's British army in the French and Indian War. The last time had been when Morgan and his Virginia riflemen had marched from Cambridge with Benedict Arnold, headed for Quebec.

At Cambridge, Nathanael had come to have the same high regard for Morgan that he had for Israel Putnam. Each spoke the countryman's language, laced with homely wit. They put on no airs, relished a good fight, and did not know the meaning of fear. Nathanael not only liked Morgan, but he had a tremendous respect for his fighting abilities.

They greeted each other affectionately. Morgan was only six years older than Nathanael, still lean and hard of muscle, but now he had a crooked way of walking that twisted his face into a grimace of pain.

He sank gratefully into a chair. "Got a misery in my legs," he explained. "Started when I was up in Canada. This country hereabouts don't help it, neither. Wetter'n the bottom of a well. Gits into my joints."

Nathanael was dismayed. "I hope it won't keep you from the field, General . . . I've some plans for you. . . ."

Morgan grinned. "Reckon I'll git there. What's your design?"

"We're not strong enough yet to meet the enemy in a major battle. I've decided to send you with a force to annoy him. It will give me a chance to build up the main body to fighting strength while you keep Cornwallis busy watching you from his camp in Winnsboro."

A frown wrinkled Morgan's forehead. "I don't like it, General. Dividing up your army could git you in trouble. If Cornwallis was to give my men a bad beating, then he'd have no trouble in finishing off yours."

"I must take that risk," said Nathanael. "I count on you, General Morgan, to avoid a major battle. I want you to harass Cornwallis, keep provisions, cattle, and horses out of his hands, frighten the Tories thereabouts from joining the enemy, and encourage the militia to come out and aid us. When the rest of our army is ready, we'll join you and meet the British."

Morgan still shook his head dubiously, but Nathanael's mind was made up. Meanwhile, Kosciusko had selected an excellent new camp site about 80 miles to the southeast, on the Pee Dee. It was in a position to threaten British-held Camden, as well as Cornwallis's communications with Charleston. And it was in country where it would be easier to obtain food.

Daniel Morgan had not exaggerated when he spoke of the region's wetness in that winter season. When all was ready for the army's departure from Charlotte, it began to rain. The downpour continued for eleven days. At last, on December 19, the weather cleared and the army marched.

At the same time Morgan set out for the west. He had only about 600 men, but they were good troops, mostly Continentals and battle-seasoned militia. They included 80 mounted Continental dragoons under the commander in chief's distant relative, Colonel William Washington.

The main army floundered toward the Pee Dee. Its horses, hauling wagons which had been rounded up, were little more than skin and bones for lack of food. Time after time, the men, who were not much better off, had to put their shoulders to the wheels to free the vehicles, stuck in clinging mud that seemed bottomless. It was a week before the long column, looking like an immense, rust-colored worm, reached the new camp site.

There officers and men alike toiled day and night to build barracks and forage for provisions. Meanwhile, Morgan was deep in the enemy's territory. He had crossed the Catawba and Broad rivers, and he reported he had reached a point not many miles from Cornwallis's camp at Winnsboro.

In the camp on the Pee Dee food was more plentiful. Supplies and a few reinforcements were trickling in. Nathanael strove feverishly to put the army into shape for action. He tightened discipline and had the men drilled constantly. Once they had clothing that at least covered their nakedness, they held their heads higher.

Then a young officer rode into camp, followed by 280 cavalry and infantry in short green jackets, white linen breeches, and tall bearskin caps. Their commander, Lieutenant Colonel Henry Lee, was a muscular fellow, blond with alert blue eyes. He was clad in a bright green jacket, lambskin breeches, boots whose high polish had somehow defied the mud, and a leather cap in which a tall horsehair plume waved jauntily. Nathanael had known "Light Horse Harry," as everyone called him, during the campaign around Philadelphia. He was delighted that Washington had detached Lee's Legion and sent it southward to aid him. Light Horse Harry was a bold, resourceful fighter, and his men would follow him anywhere.

Nevertheless, Nathanael had much to worry him. He had violated a cardinal rule of military strategy in dividing his army. As far as its fighting ability was concerned, he had full confidence in his officers and in the Continentals, but of the militia he was not so sure. . . . And if Cornwallis could destroy or cripple Morgan's force, all would be lost.

Now disturbing news reached the camp. Marion's alert scouts reported that Major General Alexander Leslie had reached Charleston with 1500 British troops and was marching to join Cornwallis.

Then, during the latter part of January, a courier sent by Morgan rode into the American camp. "We've won a big victory, sir!" the messenger told Nathanael. "Cornwallis sent the Green Dragoon after us with 1100 men. They caught up with us at the Cowpens. We've almost destroyed Tarleton's Legion—killed a hundred, wounded two hundred, and captured seven hundred."

"What of Morgan's force?" Nathanael demanded breathlessly.

The messenger grinned. "We lost twelve killed and sixty wounded. Here's a report of it from General Morgan."

"Where is Morgan now?"

"Retreating northward, sir. When Cornwallis heard of the fight he started after us with his main army. General Morgan will wait for your army at the Catawba River as long as possible."

Nathanael knew that in spite of his smashing victory, Morgan was in a precarious situation. Like Israel Putnam, the Virginian was brave, venturesome, a formidable foe in battle, but he had little knowledge of military strategy—directing the movements of an army. He was going to need help in order to elude Cornwallis.

Nathanael called Isaac Huger to headquarters. "You will take command of the army, General," he said. "Make all preparations and march as soon as you can up the Yadkin River. I'm leaving at once to join General Morgan. We'll make a junction with you at Salisbury."

He also sent a dispatch to Colonel Carrington in Richmond, telling him to collect all boats possible along the Dan River. They might be of crucial importance in case the army had to fall back all the way to Virginia.

With that, accompanied by his two aides, a sergeant, and small guard of dragoons, Nathanael rode out of the camp on his dash of over a hundred miles through the wilderness to intercept Morgan on his northward march.

Nathanael Greene's great retreat had begun.

★ ★ ★ ★ ★ ★ ★ ★ ★ ★ ★ ★ ★ ★ ★ ★ ★ ★

> *. . . the quarry never found*
> *Is still a fever to the quest-*
> *ing hound . . .*
> JOHN MASEFIELD

This was what had happened at the Cowpens:

There had been more grumbling than usual among Daniel Morgan's men on January 16, though it was not because they had to march all day through a cold, misty drizzle. Wet weather was nothing new to them. What they resented was that they had had to leave their breakfasts cooking over the fires when a report reached the camp on the Pacolet River that the British were coming.

"What's Morgan a-runnin' for?" demanded one of the Maryland Continentals. "Time was he'd of stood and fought like a cornered possum. He was tough enough for a spell there—a-hangin' all them deserters. But look at him now, way back at the tail end of the column. You'd think he was scairt."

"You know he's got the rheumatiz all over him," said his mate severely. "Why, he couldn't scarcely mount his horse this mornin'. But don't you worry about old Morgan. He ain't scairt. Mark you, if it comes to a fight he'll be right in there with us."

About sundown the rain ceased. Morgan, riding in the rear at a slow walk because of the pain that almost doubled him up, ordered a halt for the night in a clearing alongside the road. It was known as the Cowpens because it had once been a place where cattle were assembled before being driven to market.

About dusk, a clatter of hoofs resounded from down the road. It was General Pickens, riding in with his band of partisans.

The pain-racked Morgan managed a grin. "I'm glad to see ye, General. Thought first 'twas Benny (he meant Banastre Tarleton). He's heading this way with his Green Dragoons and some Regulars. There'll be a fight in the morning, sure. I've had a few militia join me, but I can use your men."

Andrew Pickens did not reply. A taciturn man with a hooked nose and a long, lugubrious face more suited to a New England Puritan, he was known never to use one word when none would do.

His men wore the deerskin, leather, and homespun of the wilderness, with coonskin caps on their heads. Some had no guns or swords, and carried pitchforks, reaping hooks, or scythes in their places. But they could fight like catamounts, as Morgan well knew.

"'Tain't the best ground for a fight," he went on. "Ye can see there's no woods 'round the clearing thick enough to cover a retreat. But it's likely these militia of mine'll run for it, quick as they ketch a whiff of burnt powder. Well they won't git far. No place to hide, and the Broad River's just a piece back from here. With all this rain it'll be too high for 'em to cross."

Before his men lay down with their guns beside them, Morgan arranged them in a battle formation of three lines. Near the foot of a slope on the field, facing the approaching enemy, he placed his first line—Georgia and South Carolina militia. Back of them, part way up the slope, he posted Pickens's men, and just below its crest he put the troops upon whom he most depended—the Delaware and Maryland Continentals.

Hobbling like an old woman, he made his way up and down the lines, encouraging the men and joking with them. One injunction he repeated over and over to the militiamen: "Only thing I want of ye, boys, is to give 'em two volleys. Two volleys, hear? Then ye can fall back."

Most of the men slept, but not their commander. It was Morgan himself who roused them at dawn: "Up, boys, up! Benny's comin'."

The enemy came in the cold gray light—two battalions of battle-tested Regulars advancing in a long red line with inflexible precision. On their flanks, Tarleton's green-coated dragoons and British cavalry spurred their mounts to a gallop.

The militia stood their ground. Behind them, Morgan rode up and down, shouting, "Don't fire! Don't fire yet!" Then, remembering Israel Putnam's famous words at Bunker Hill, he repeated them: "Don't fire till ye see the whites of their eyes!"

A ferocious shout rose from the advancing enemy. "They give us the British halloo!" Morgan yelled. "Take aim and give 'em the injun halloo!"

The war whoop shrilled over the battlefield. "Fire!" Morgan cried.

He got his two volleys; some fired three. The bullets tore great holes in the British line, but it kept on. The unseasoned militia, remembering Morgan's promise, turned and ran up the slope.

Pickens's men took up the fight. Morgan urged them to concentrate on the British officers: "Look for the epaulets! Pick off the epaulets!"

They too fired two or three volleys and retired. The British cavalrymen galloped in to cut them down with their sabers. But Morgan had stationed Colonel Washington and his cavalry to the rear in readiness for just such an attack. They swept forward in a charge so fierce and unexpected that the British riders found themselves being

88

slashed to pieces. They fled, with Washington's men after them.

Now it was the Continentals of the third line who faced the oncoming red-coated infantry. Behind them, Morgan and Pickens were trying to reform the retreating militia. "Form! Form!" Morgan bellowed. "Give 'em one more volley and the day is ours! Old Morgan was never beat!"

They rallied and took their place on the right of the Continentals, who had been forced to fall back, and whose commander now ordered: "Give them the bayonet!"

They surged forward. The British line collapsed before the ferocity of the charge. Colonel Washington's cavalry, giving up their pursuit of the British riders, wheeled and met a desperate charge by Tarleton's dragoons, driving them from the field. The fight was won.

Morgan had captured a rich booty—35 wagonloads of baggage and supplies, abandoned by the fleeing British, 100 of the dragoons' horses, 800 fine muskets, and the two brass cannon the enemy had on the field. About 150 of Tarleton's force escaped, but Morgan dared not follow. He knew that Cornwallis, not far to the south, would be after him with the main army as soon as he received the shocking news of the defeat. Thus he must not only save his force from the British, but somehow get his 700 prisoners to a place where they would be safe from rescue.

Luckily, Cornwallis decided to wait for General Leslie and his 1500 reinforcements. It was two days before they reached Winnsboro and the chase could begin.

Morgan left Colonel Pickens and his men behind to hinder the enemy as much as possible. Then he marched into North Carolina with all speed. It rained all the way, but it was the weather which finally gave him a chance to rest his tired and mud-bespattered men. The Catawba River was rising as it came brawling out of the mountains. When Cornwallis reached it, two days after Morgan had crossed, it was impassable. The Americans were safe on the east bank, and there, on January 30, Nathanael and his party rode into the camp at Sherrill's Ford.

He asked eager, searching questions about Cowpens, especially the plan of battle which had been used. Morgan might be no military strategist, but his tactics—the science of drawing up troops and directing them in battle—had been perfect.

"What about Lord Cornwallis?" Nathanael asked. "Do you know his intentions?"

"Why," said Morgan, "he'll be after us soon's the river falls, General. My scouts report he's burnt his baggage."

*"What's that?"* Nathanael demanded incredulously.

"Everything he can possibly git along without—even most of his wagons."

"Then he is ours!" cried Nathanael. "Without his baggage, every mile he moves northward the worse off he'll be. We'll retreat and draw him far away from his supply depots in South Carolina. Then, when we get enough reinforcements, we'll attack him. But we can't let him catch us till we're ready."

"Aye," said Morgan, "we'd better git moving."

"Do you have an idea of where Cornwallis will cross when the river falls?"

"He's camped near Beattie's Ford," said Morgan, "but there's four other crossings thereabouts. Davidson's come in from Charlotte with about 800 men. I sent him to guard all the fords. And he's got 50 cavalry across the river, watching the British."

Nathanael was heartened by this news of the brigadier

general he had left at Charlotte with a small force when the rest of the army marched for the Pee Dee. William Davidson was an able and dependable militia officer. And he must have been able to recruit some additional militia around Charlotte.

"What of your prisoners?" Nathanael asked Morgan.

"Safe, General, well to the north of here."

"Good," said Nathanael. "March your force toward Salisbury. I'm going over and talk to Davidson."

He rode through a driving rain the next day to Davidson's camp at Beattie's Ford. Paying no heed to the downpour, the two walked to the edge of the river. There they sat on a fallen log and talked.

"Cornwallis can move faster than we can without his baggage," said Nathanael. "Hinder him all you can when he crosses. It will give General Morgan time to get away."

"The British are camped just across from us, and 'twould seem they design to cross here," Davidson told him.

"Cornwallis may be up to something," Nathanael warned. "If he sends cavalry across at one of the other fords, you'll be in trouble if they get in your rear. Have your cavalry patrol the river through the night."

The two men decided that either Beattie's or Cowan's Ford was the one Cornwallis was most likely to use. Nathanael had carefully studied Kosciusko's survey of the river. After he had left, Davidson shook his head in amazement. "General Greene has never been on the Catawba before," he remarked to one of his officers, "but he appears to know more about it than men who have been raised on its banks."

Before leaving, Nathanael said to Davidson, "If the

British succeed in crossing and you are forced back, meet me with your militia at David Carr's tavern on the Salisbury road." Then he mounted and rode off upstream.

Davidson left 250 of his troops at Beattie's Ford and took 250 others four miles down the river to Cowan's, along with 50 of his cavalry. Small detachments were guarding the other fords.

He posted a picket of 25 men along the river's edge at Cowan's to watch for the British. The rest he took to the rear, a short distance upstream.

Joel Jetton and Robert Henry, two of the picket, lay in an open space surrounded by a jungle of haw, cane, and persimmon near the river bank. They were of the same age, barely sixteen, and lived on neighboring farms along the river not many miles away.

It was pitch dark now. Huddling close to the warmth of their fire, they could see other watch fires the rest of the picket had built. The flames sent fitful gleams out over the black water, revealing white rips like bared teeth where the river boiled over submerged rocks and ledges.

Suddenly Joel jumped nervously. He jerked himself to a sitting position and gazed out over the river.

"Ye hear something, Joel?" Robert half-whispered. His voice trembled.

"Thought I did. Listen . . ."

But the only sound that came to their ears was the roar of the swollen river. If there was anything on the opposite bank it was lost in the darkness, 500 yards away.

"Joel . . ." Robert quavered. "Are ye scairt?"

"Naw," the other boy replied, but his voice belied it. "Are ye?"

"Maybe . . . a little. What if the Green Dragoons was to come across here? They say they'll slice your head in half with their sabers quicker'n ye could split a punkin with an axe."

Joel didn't reply. He reached out for his musket and made sure the bayonet he had fashioned from a pitchfork was securely fastened to the barrel.

"Where d'ye s'pose they'll cross if they come this way?" Robert asked.

"I know this ford. There's two crossings. One comes straight over, but it's deep at high water. T'other slants upstream. It's longer, but not so deep. Likely Tories've told Cornwallis about it and he'll use that one."

The commander of the picket came crashing out of the brush. "If you see or hear anything, fire a signal shot to alarm General Davidson's men," he told them. "After that, don't waste your ammunition till they're within musket range." Then he disappeared into the night.

In spite of their fears, the two boys soon fell asleep. Dawn was streaking the eastern horizon when Joel woke with a start. As he listened, a splashing sound above the roar of the river brought him bolt upright. He scrambled to his feet and ran to the water's edge. The sentry who had been posted there was stretched out, fast asleep.

Then Joel saw them . . . *men out there, right in mid-stream!*

He primed his gun and pulled the trigger. It missed fire. Joel dashed back toward the rest of the sleeping picket, shouting, "The British! The British!" He tried the musket again. This time it went off.

Now Joel could see the enemy more clearly, wading waist-deep in the flood. First came figures in countrymen's dress—they would be Tory guides who knew the way through the shallower water. Behind them was an impressive figure in scarlet and white, mounted on a magnificent horse. Joel drew in his breath—Cornwallis!

93

Behind the general a red-coated column floundered four abreast, led by another officer on horseback. These troops had their muskets lashed high on their shoulders, the bayonets fixed. They carried long staves to steady themselves against the rampaging current.

Joel reloaded, drew a bead on Cornwallis and fired. But in his excitement his aim was bad, though the shot hit the horse. It staggered, but managed to stay on its feet and plunged on. Muskets were popping all up and down the line of the picket now.

The two boys made each shot count. The enemy, struggling against the current, was unable to return the fire. Exhilaration banished Joel's fear. Why, this was more fun than a turkey shoot!

The British column seemed to be in confusion. Men hit by bullets fell and vanished in the black torrent. So did others who stepped into treacherous holes in the river's rocky bed and were swept away and drowned.

Joel saw an officer's horse lose its footing. It rolled over, throwing its rider off, and was carried downstream, struggling helplessly. Another officer's horse met the same fate.

Suddenly Joel uttered a cry of dismay. The Tory guides had lost their way. Instead of leading the British column over the shallower, oblique crossing, they had taken the more dangerous one directly across the Catawba.

For the enemy it was a lucky mistake. At the signal shot, General Davidson had led his force to the place upstream where he expected the British to land. Without their aid, the 25 men of the picket could not stop Cornwallis's army.

The British commander's horse dropped dead as it reached shore, but he was safe. In spite of the deep water, his soldiers were piling ashore behind him. First came the shock troops, then the crack light infantry of the Brigade of Guards, followed by a regiment of Hessians, the Royal Welsh Fusileers, and last the dreaded Green Dragoons.

Although Tarleton's force had been greatly reduced in the fight at the Cowpens, it was now reinforced. The sight of the green-coated riders broke the two boys' nerve. As they turned in panic and ran, they were not alone. The whole picket was fleeing.

Meanwhile, General Davidson and his men, heading for the point above the picket where the British were expected to come ashore, heard the firing downstream and veered toward it at a furious pace. The fleeing militia of the picket went by them even faster, in the opposite direction.

Davidson led his infantry forward, leaving his cavalry on a ridge to the rear in case the enemy cavalry should try to get behind his force. The British, almost all ashore now, sent a volley crashing into the Americans' ranks, but they kept on.

Davidson had plunged ahead toward the riverbank. Just then a single shot rang out. Seated on his mount, the general stared with a puzzled expression at a redcoat holding a smoking musket. With that, he plunged off his horse, dead from the bullet the man had fired.

His men, seeing their leader fall, were thrown into panic. Their line buckled and they too fled in disorder.

About 500 of the routed militia tried to obey the order to meet Nathanael on the Salisbury road. But when they reached a tavern about seven miles from the rendezvous, they were so spent from running that they had to stop and rest.

A few minutes later, the lookout they had posted gave the alarm. It was Tarleton's corps approaching. The militia had the courage to fire a well-directed volley which staggered the Green Dragoons. Then their valor failed them and they scattered in all directions. This time they did not stop.

Thus when Nathanael arrived at David Carr's tavern, the militia were not there. He waited hopefully all the afternoon and evening. At midnight a militia officer rode in.

"We lost the fight at Cowan's Ford, sir!" he burst out. "General Davidson was killed. Cornwallis is marching for Salisbury."

"And your men?" Nathanael demanded.

"Running for it, General."

Nathanael mounted and spurred his horse to a reckless gallop. After an all-night ride he reached Steele's Tavern in Salisbury. His friend Dr. William Read, a surgeon in charge of an army hospital which had been established there, greeted him: "What! Are you alone, General?"

Nathanael's head was bowed in despair. "Aye," he replied, "tired, hungry, alone, and penniless."

Patriotic Mrs. Steele overheard him. "Now, you sit right down, General, and we'll fix that," she said.

She went into the kitchen, returning to put a bountiful, smoking breakfast before him. She also had two little cloth bags which clinked when she set them on the table. They were filled with money—hard money.

"Take these, for I can do without them," she said.

On the wall of the dining room hung a portrait of King George III of England. It had remained since the time when Americans thought of him as their kind and fatherly ruler. Nathanael rose, turned the King's face to the wall, snatched up a piece of charcoal from the hearth and wrote on the back of the picture, "Hide thy head, George, and blush."

As he ate, he asked Dr. Read about Morgan and his force.

"Making all speed for the Yadkin River," the surgeon replied.

Nathanael was outraged by the flight of the militia. He sent off a letter to Steuben in Virginia, telling him what had happened. "These are some of the unhappy effects of defending the country with militia," he added, "from which the good Lord deliver us!"

Then he galloped toward the Yadkin, seven miles away. His horse had trouble keeping its feet in the dreary red morass that had once been a road. He thought of how the slippery, clinging mud would impede Morgan's force. And the river, he knew, would be swollen by the rains.

Anxiety gnawed at him like an ulcer. More than once he turned in his saddle, fearful of seeing the cavalry of the British advance guard approaching. Everything now depended upon Morgan's reaching the Yadkin and crossing in time.

At last the river's swirling brown flood loomed ahead of him. He tensed as he saw a horde of men on the bank there at Trading Fork Ford. Morgan's men. . . .

Then he saw boats. Some were crossing, loaded with soldiers, horses or baggage, some returning empty for new loads.

Morgan's fierce grin helped to ease Nathanael's concern. "Good thing ye ordered them flatboats built to carry with us, General," the Old Wagoner said. "We rounded up a few more 'long the river, but we could use more. Looks as if we'd git the boys over in time, though."

Just in time, it turned out. Getting all the men, wagons, and horses over in the scant supply of boats was slow work. The last of them had just pushed off when the British advance reached Trading Fork Ford.

Nathanael had gone to a small cabin a short distance back from the river's edge and was busy writing a dispatch to General Huger, ordering him to veer off his course toward Salisbury and march instead for Guilford Courthouse, near the Virginia border. Thunder split the night and orange flashes lighted the blackness across the river. The enemy's cannon were hurling shot at the Americans' side.

Morgan, who was with Nathanael, chuckled. "I dunno what good it'll do 'em to waste powder and ball shooting at what they can't see."

The cabin was partly shielded by a pile of rocks, but its roof protruded above them. Suddenly, with a tremendous slam, a cannon ball struck the roof, sending up a shower of timbers and splinters.

"Lucky shot," Morgan barked. "That Britainer's mad as a wet hen because we fooled him."

Nathanael's quill went right on scratching as if nothing had happened, but he was thankful that Cornwallis had been held up long enough for Morgan to escape. The men would have a chance to catch their breaths before the race continued.

A desperate race it would be, nevertheless. Cornwallis could only be halted until the Yadkin subsided, or he moved his army to one of the shallower fords farther upstream. The Americans were in no condition yet to stand and fight. Their headlong retreat before the fast-moving enemy must go on.

# 9

*One more river! There's one more river to cross!* CHANT OF GRADUATING CLASS, U.S. NAVAL ACADEMY, BEFORE FINAL EXAMINATION

On the other side of the Yadkin, the frustrated Cornwallis waited in hopes that the flood would subside. Meanwhile, Nathanael sent Morgan ahead toward Guilford Courthouse with his light infantry. The rest of the force moved north a few miles. There, with enough distance between them and the enemy to give them a headstart, Nathanael waited for intelligence of Cornwallis's movements.

He wrote to the partisan leaders: Marion was to continue making an infernal nuisance of himself with his sorties against British posts in South Carolina; Andrew Pickens, now somewhere south of the Broad River, was to move across it, raise militia and worry the rear of Cornwallis's army.

Temperamental Thomas Sumter had recovered from his wound, but he had made no move with his corps. He was angry because Nathanael had appointed Morgan to command in the region west of the Catawba, which Sumter considered his territory. Nathanael wrote him a cordial, soothing letter, urging him to send his backwoodsmen against the enemy's rear.

He also addressed urgent appeals for volunteers to North Carolina and Virginia. He needed reinforcements desperately, for he hoped to make a stand against the

99

British when Huger's main army arrived. The loss of brave General Davidson not only saddened him, but it was a serious misfortune. The militia of the Carolinas had trusted him, and would turn out to fight as they would for no one else.

The Americans had crossed the Yadkin on February 3. Three days later, Nathanael's intelligence reported that Cornwallis was on the move. He had given up hope that the river would recede enough to permit a crossing at Trading Fork Ford, and his army was headed for the shallower fords upstream. Nathanael breathed more easily. The British general's roundabout route would give the Americans a little advantage in the race.

The army marched for Guilford Courthouse. Not only was Morgan there, but the main army under Isaac Huger had arrived. With them had come Light Horse Harry Lee's Legion, recalled from South Carolina, where it had aided Francis Marion in a daring but unsuccessful attempt to capture British-held Georgetown on the coast.

Huger's army was a ragged horde, many barefoot and limping from frostbite. The horses were skeletons, their patched and mended harness barely holding together. The wagons they had somehow dragged for more than a hundred miles, overloaded with the sick, were falling apart, with wheels that wobbled crazily.

Nor was the sight of Daniel Morgan reassuring when Nathanael called a war council at the rude little courthouse in the tiny hamlet. The old warrior dragged himself in crabwise, his face contorted with agony.

Nevertheless, Nathanael was determined on action, now that his army was safely reunited. "Gentlemen," he said, "I believe we should make our stand here against Lord Cornwallis. I have been over the ground, and it is an excellent place for a battle."

There was an immediate rumble of dissent from his officers—Lee, William Washington, Edward Carrington, and others. "Impossible, General!" Huger cried. "You've seen my men. How can they fight now?"

"They seem in good spirits," Nathanael countered.

"What's left of 'em are," said Huger. "Along the last of the march there wasn't a day went by that a lot of 'em didn't desert. Why, there's only 36 men left out of one company that was 300 strong leaving the Pee Dee."

Others chimed in to support Huger. Nathanael turned hopefully toward Morgan. The Old Wagoner had never dodged a battle. "What do you think, General?"

Morgan shook his head. "Ye better wait."

"Do you know Cornwallis's present strength, General?" Huger asked.

"My intelligence indicates he has between 2500 and 3000 men."

"Aye," said Huger, "and they're better trained and equipped than ours. What's our present strength?"

"A little over 2000," Nathanael answered, "though we've got about 1400 Continentals."

"What about reinforcements?"

Nathanael's face darkened. "I've been expecting some, but Baron von Steuben informs me he's having trouble recruiting in Virginia. The people are worried about Benedict Arnold, and they want their militia at home to defend them."

He too was worried about Arnold. From New York, General Clinton had sent the traitor, now a British army general, to Virginia on a raiding expedition. If Arnold could get behind the retreating American army, the result could be disastrous.

On sober reflection, Nathanael saw that he had let his hopes get the better of his judgment. At least, he reflected, if the army could escape Cornwallis, it would be close to its principal base of supplies and reinforcements in Virginia, while the British commander would be some 200 miles from his nearest one on the North Carolina coast.

He scanned a map spread on the table before him. He knew what the roads would be like in this season, with the constant rains showing no sign of letting up. The route to Virginia lay through countryside thickly laced with creeks and the swamplands along their borders. Cornwallis, traveling with little or no baggage, could make far greater speed. And there, meandering back and forth across the North Carolina–Virginia border, was the wide, deep River Dan.

"You are right, gentlemen," he told his officers. "We must continue to retreat. Once we are in Virginia . . ." His voice trailed off. He did not dare to hazard a prediction of what would happen then, for he knew this would be the most desperate race of all.

"Colonel Carrington," he said, "you are familiar with the Dan. Where is our best crossing?"

The quartermaster stepped forward. "There are two good ones, General—Dix's Ferry, and below it, Boyd's." His finger indicated them on the map.

"We will cross at the lower one," Nathanael decided. "Ride with all speed to Dix's Ferry, Colonel. Collect its boats and any others you can find along the river; if the enemy is close behind us, our flatboats will not be enough. Float the boats downstream to our crossing at Boyd's Ferry."

Nathanael also ordered Kosciusko to ride ahead with a small detachment to throw up a breastwork at the ferry. He hoped it would not be needed . . .

Then he spoke to Morgan: "It is my design to divide the army again. We will throw 700 light troops in Lord

Cornwallis's path to hinder him until the rest of the army and the baggage can be gotten over the river. You will command them, General."

When Morgan tried to reply, the words seemed to choke him. At last he shook his head sadly and muttered, "Ye know I've never feared a fight, General Greene, but ye can't fight an enemy ye can't see, like this one inside me"—he pointed to his crippled legs. "Ye better git somebody else."

This Nathanael had been dreading after seeing the ravages of Morgan's ailment. His heart was heavy over the loss of this rugged fighter who had been a bastion of strength to him. He nodded sorrowfully, and spoke to another of his officers.

"Colonel Williams, you will command the light troops."

Morgan could never be replaced, but Nathanael had full confidence in this veteran of many a battle. He had first known Otho Williams at Cambridge in 1775; then at Fort Washington, when Williams's Maryland troops had held the Hessians at bay until their overheated muskets were useless. He had fought brilliantly in the South at Camden and King's Mountain.

"You will shield the main army at all costs," Nathanael told Williams. "Destroy the bridges over the creeks on Lord Cornwallis's route and seize all horses and provisions that might fall into his hands. The safety of the whole army will depend upon how well you can harass the enemy and at the same time avoid a full battle."

Daniel Morgan had some parting words of advice for Nathanael. "Ye have a great number of militia, General," he said. "If they fight, ye will beat Cornwallis; if not, he'll beat ye and perhaps cut your Continentals to pieces. When ye meet the British, I think ye ought to put the militia in the center, and have some picked troops behind 'em with orders to shoot the first man that runs. That'd ought to make 'em stand and fight."

His disarming smile softened his ferocious expression. "Hope ye don't think I'm meddling, General. I just want to see ye beat Cornwallis."

Nathanael thanked him with heartfelt gratitude. He would not forget the advice. Then the Old Wagoner took up his sore and weary journey to his home in Virginia.

Otho Williams marched west to place himself in front of the oncoming British. He had the best men of the army—240 cavalry under Colonel Washington, 280 Continentals led by Colonel John Eager Howard, and 60 sharpshooters from the Virginia mountains under Colonel William Campbell.

The same day the main army set out for the Dan River crossing, 70 miles away. The Americans marched through the dreary winter landscape in a pelting rain. As the mud grew deeper, the road ahead of the toiling army was like a long, narrow lake. Nathanael knew Cornwallis would be gaining ground, free of the load of baggage and the heavy flatboats his own army was carrying.

Yet the constant downpour cheered him. The Dan would surely be impassable by wading. If he could reach it in time to cross ahead of the enemy . . . if Carrington succeeded in rounding up boats—boats Cornwallis might otherwise use—the British would be forced to march well up the river to the shallower fords there.

Soon after the army left Guilford Courthouse, a messenger from Otho Williams dashed in. "The British are starting their march before dawn each morning, General," he reported. Later, a second dispatch rider brought the word: "Cornwallis has abandoned more of his baggage. His army has orders to march 25 miles a day."

The British commander, sure he could overhaul the Americans, had reckoned without Otho Williams. The Maryland leader handled his detachment like a magician who makes his audience see things that are not there. Cornwallis could never be sure that the force ahead of him was not the entire American army, moved suddenly westward to block his passage.

Williams ducked, dodged, backtracked, and used every trick of the hunted fox. He would place his detachment across the road ahead of the British advance force, consisting of Tarleton's Green Dragoons and Hessian yagers. There, from concealment, his men would pick off Tarleton's horses. To the rear, Cornwallis would have to halt and rearrange his main body to meet a possible ambush by the whole enemy army. It cost him precious hours.

When night fell, the Americans melted away into the underbrush. Cornwallis was heading for the upper fords of the Dan. His spies had convinced him the Americans would have to march upstream too. Between his road and that taken by the American main army ran a third road. Here Williams would make his camp at nightfall.

What he feared was a surprise attack by darkness. His camp bristled with a ring of sentries, and patrols watched the British through each night. In the morning he would begin his march even earlier than the enemy, moving at high speed. After a march of several miles, he would halt so the men could enjoy an unhurried breakfast. Then they would return to their game of stinging the British column like a plague of gadflies.

But Williams's men were tiring. So many were needed to stand night sentry duty watches that no one got much sleep. Each day's march was exhausting, for Cornwallis not only started early but continued several hours after nightfall. When the Americans were able to halt for a short rest, the soldiers would fling themselves on the cold, muddy ground and be instantly asleep.

At last Williams received a dispatch ordering him to veer to the eastward and join the main army, which was approaching the Dan. But Cornwallis's advance force, close behind, saw the move. The British took up the pursuit.

Light Horse Harry Lee's Legion formed Williams's rear guard. For more than a mile they galloped across country with the enemy cavalry in sight behind them. Lee ordered a small detachment of his cavalry to remain in the rear. They held off the enemy long enough for the rest of the Legion to escape.

Night fell, but the chase continued. Suddenly, out of the darkness ahead, loomed many campfires. Williams was almost paralyzed with consternation. It could only be the main army's camp. Before they could be alarmed and ready to fight, the British would be upon them.

Williams halted and gathered his officers about him for a hasty council. "Let us make a stand and give the main army a chance to escape," one suggested. The others agreed.

Williams hesitated. He had received several dispatches from Nathanael reminding him that he must on no account risk the destruction of his detachment, for with it would go all the hopes of the entire army. Yet in first assigning him the mission, Nathanael had said, "You will shield the main army at all costs." What should he do?

Just then a rider from the vanguard galloped up. "The campfires are deserted, sir!" he cried. "The main army has moved on."

There was no explanation for the burning fires, save that friendly farmers in the neighborhood might have

106

kept them going so that Williams's detachment might use them when it came up.

But there was no stopping for them. Cornwallis was still in pursuit. A little later the rear guard reported the British had halted. The Americans too made camp. The men slept on their arms and a constant patrol was set. They had only a short time to rest. At midnight the British took up the chase again, and the Americans fled before them.

Morning came. There was no rain, but the countryside was enveloped in eerie mist. Williams peered ahead, wondering desperately how much farther it was. Had the main army reached the Dan?

At that moment Nathanael Greene was beset by a worry of a different kind. Riding at the head of the long, plodding column, he could see ahead through the fog the outline of an earthwork and knew it must be the one he had ordered thrown up at the ferry. Would the boats be there . . . ? If they were not, his army, with its back to the river, would be forced to fight a hopeless, disastrous battle.

The boats were there. Breathing a thankful prayer, Nathanael turned in his saddle to shout the good news.

At two o'clock that afternoon, Otho Williams received a dispatch from Nathanael: "The greater part of the wagons are over, and the troops are crossing." Early that evening came another: "All our troops are over and the stage is clear. I am ready to receive and give you a hearty welcome."

That night the American army slept in peace and safety on the north bank of the Dan. Nathanael Greene's great retreat was over. His gamble at such long odds had won; that of Cornwallis, when he had destroyed his baggage, had lost when he was within a hair's breadth of triumph.

This, in truth, was a retreat to victory. Just how far-reaching were its results would not be known for a long time. But even now there was cause for rejoicing in America.

Cornwallis was so far from his bases that there was no chance of receiving supplies from them. His troops' clothing was becoming tattered and his ammunition growing scant. The countryside was so ravaged that he could not depend upon it to subsist his army. He had been beaten as surely as if he had been routed in a major engagement.

# 10 ★ ★ ★ ★ ★ ★ ★ ★ ★ ★ ★ ★ ★ ★ ★ ★ ★ ★

*Another such victory would destroy
the British army.* CHARLES JAMES FOX

Nathanael had brought his miserable army safely
through 200 miles of constant rain, mud as tenacious as
quicksand and solitary wilderness. He had lost none of the
army's baggage. Morgan's British prisoners were safe in
jail, well to the north. And Nathanael had Cornwallis
where he wanted him, in a net the British commander had
spread for himself by the rash destruction of his baggage
and the distance he had put between himself and his
supply bases.

Nathanael had good news for his officers at a council
not long after the army crossed the Dan.

"We shall soon have substantial reinforcements," he
announced. "The people hereabouts are alarmed now that
Lord Cornwallis threatens Virginia. Governor Jefferson
has called out all the militia in the southern part of the
state. And I am informed that other militia companies are
collecting in North Carolina to join us."

"Will they come?" someone asked.

"Eight hundred Virginia militia are on the way, as well
as a thousand sharpshooters from the mountains to the
west."

Colonel Carrington looked worried. "I have few muskets to arm them, General."

"The mountaineers will have their own hunting rifles.

As for the militia, we will hope they will come equipped with guns. . . ."

Colonel Washington spoke up: "The shortage of horses is most severe, sir. Many of my cavalry are not mounted. If we could only obtain some here . . . no finer horses are bred anywhere."

Nathanael smiled. "I was about to order you to round them up, Colonel. Governor Jefferson has given me permission to requisition the horses from the inhabitants."

A grin spread over Washington's face. "Very good, sir! They'll scream bloody murder over it, but just leave it to me."

"Are we to retreat farther north, General?" asked one of the officers.

"It will depend upon what Lord Cornwallis does. The river is beginning to fall. If he crosses it, we will retreat until enough reinforcements join us to make a stand."

Another asked, "Do you think he will cross, General?"

"I doubt it. He is already in enough trouble, so far from his bases."

"And if he retreats, sir?"

"We will follow."

"In that case, do you think he will fight?"

"I am sure of it," said Nathanael. "That was his objective in pursuing us."

On February 19, just four days after the Americans had crossed the Dan, the British army began its retreat.

Nathanael ordered Light Horse Harry Lee and his Legion back across the river. They were to join Andrew Pickens, who had been hanging on the enemy rear during the retreat from the Yadkin.

By that time Colonel Washington had seized the horses that were needed. As he had predicted, the Virginia horse breeders were outraged, especially since he took only the best. But his cavalry and those of Lee's Legion now had the finest mounts in America, much better than those of Cornwallis's riders.

Some of the promised reinforcements were coming in. So were supplies from the rich farmlands around the American camp. The soldiers were better fed now, and rest had done them good.

Lee and Pickens headed toward Hillsboro, North Carolina, where Cornwallis was camped. By nightfall their force lay concealed along the road between Hillsboro and the upper fords of the Haw River to the west.

That night the sentinels posted on the road heard an approaching clatter of hoofbeats. They were surprised when their challenges were answered with the proper password. It was Nathanael, riding with a small party of Washington's cavalry.

For some hours he conferred with Lee and Pickens, anxious to know what their scouts had learned of the enemy. Solemn, taciturn Andrew Pickens let Lee do the talking.

"Cornwallis has issued a proclamation to the inhabitants offering land and a bounty of money to all who will take the oath of allegiance to King George and join his army," the Virginian said. "But the people don't like the way he's searching their houses for provisions and slaughtering their livestock."

"Good," said Nathanael. "Our task now is to prevent Tories from joining him, keep him from obtaining food from the countryside, and cut off his communications so that supplies can't reach him from his base at Wilmington on the coast."

"We are watching every road into Hillsboro, General," Lee assured him.

"At the same time," Nathanael went on, "it is of the

utmost importance that you avoid an encounter with any large enemy force. I shall bring the main army across the Dan in a few days, but we cannot approach close enough to support you in case of such an engagement. Therefore, I urge you to use extreme vigilance and caution to keep out of the enemy's reach."

After more discussion, Nathanael borrowed a blanket from Pickens, wrapped himself in it, and was soon asleep. At dawn he was awakened. A patrol had reported Tarleton moving toward the Haw with a force of cavalry, infantry, and two small cannon.

"It's likely he's moving to protect Tory reinforcements marching to join Cornwallis," Lee said. "With your permission, General, I'm taking a detachment of cavalry to intercept them."

Again advising caution, Nathanael agreed. As he set off to rejoin the main army to the north, Lee and his riders galloped westward. Near the Haw River they met the Tory force marching toward Hillsboro. Its commander, Colonel John Pyle, hailed them joyfully, mistaking their green coats for those of Tarleton's dragoons.

Lee let him think so. He rode up to Pyle and dismounted, his hand outstretched. But just as he was going to demand surrender, a Tory recognized his men by the sprigs of green they wore in their hats so that they could tell each other from Tarleton's men in a fight.

The Tory shouted a warning, but it was too late. Lee's horsemen, who had already surrounded Pyle's men, fell upon them, slashing to right and left. A few of the Loyalists, including Pyle, reached the safety of the thickets, but nearly a hundred were killed and most of the others wounded.

Meanwhile, the main army prepared to march. It was a

*112*

little stronger now, for some of the mountaineer riflemen had arrived. Militia regiments from North Carolina and Virginia were on the way. On February 23 the Americans crossed the Dan and moved toward the British camp at Hillsboro.

Cornwallis did not wait for them but moved his army westward. He had managed to recruit seven companies of inhabitants around Hillsboro; now he hoped to obtain more from German settlements around the Haw River which were friendly to the British.

From Hillsboro the Americans followed the enemy westward. They camped first on County Line Creek, then moved on to High Rock Ford. Cornwallis would surely have agreed this was a fitting camp site for the pestiferous army dogging his heels, for it was located on Troublesome Creek.

The next day they caught up with the advance force led by Lee and Pickens and strengthened by more light troops under Otho Williams. Nathanael held a council to discuss strategy.

"Until more reinforcements come in, we must continue our efforts to keep the Tories hereabouts from joining the enemy," he said. "I want you, General Pickens, and Colonel Williams, to keep as close as possible to the British. You must avoid an engagement with the main army, but we can afford to risk an encounter with their cavalry. We have more riders, better mounted and better fighters than Tarleton's men. As for the main army, it is my design to keep Lord Cornwallis thoroughly confused as to our movements. If we can just hold out a little longer. . . ."

"I don't know how we can feed the horses, General," said Colonel Davie. "It is hard enough to find forage for the regular cavalry, but since the new militia and mountaineers brought their own horses. . . ." He let a hopeless gesture finish the sentence.

"Then we will send the horses away," said Nathanael firmly.

Andrew Pickens made one of his rare observations: "They won't like it."

He knew what he was talking about. The new militia, never having been in battle, were frightened out of their wits at the prospect of meeting British veterans. But with horses they had the means of fleeing to safety . . . When their mounts were sent away, the militiamen followed in hordes, and even some of the tough mountaineers deserted. Nathanael began to fear that his raw troops would melt away completely and leave him at Cornwallis's mercy.

Indeed, it was plain that the British commander hoped to catch detachments of the advance force one by one and destroy them. Otho Williams's men had a narrow escape when they got too close to the enemy's camp. Under cover of a fog, the British came after them and they barely got away.

When Nathanael heard of it, he moved the main army back to safety north of the Haw. But he was soon on the move again, carrying out his plan of confusing the British and giving them no chance to attack until he was ready.

No fox ever fooled the hounds by slier backtracking and circling than did the American army during the following eight days. No one but Nathanael himself knew each night what its movements would be tomorrow. One day it would march forward as if to attack; the next it would fall back.

It marched nearly 200 miles within a small triangle formed by Reedy Fork Creek and Troublesome Creek as they flowed toward a junction with each other. In all that time it was no more than ten or twelve miles from Guilford Courthouse. Its back-and-forth movements not only confused Cornwallis, but frightened the Tories in the neighborhood out of joining the British. They saw soldiers marching past their homes so often that they were convinced the Americans had a mighty army of at least 10,000 men.

Nathanael knew that Cornwallis favored surprise attacks before dawn. He constantly patrolled the army's outposts to make sure the sentinels were awake and alert.

Making his rounds in the darkness early one morning, he passed the tent occupied by Colonel John Greene, a Virginian who was no relation. Hearing loud snores inside, he entered and roused the officer.

"How can you sleep soundly when the enemy is so near?" he demanded.

The colonel blinked sleepily. "Why, General," he said, "I always do, for I know you will be awake."

Nathanael said later it was the greatest compliment he ever received.

During this critical maneuvering, he had to think constantly of how food could be obtained. For hours each night he would have Colonel Davie in his tent, discussing where the next day's meals for the army would come from. He lived on the same scanty, coarse food as the soldiers. Often his own supplies ran short, and he would say to one of his aides, "Go out into the camp and see if any of the boys can lend me a few provisions." The men loved him for it.

Few of the promised reinforcements had arrived. Now another blow fell. Andrew Pickens's men were so ragged they were all but naked. Unless clothing could be found for them, they could no longer serve. There was nothing

Nathanael could do but allow them to go home to South Carolina and Georgia. But Pickens promised that once they were clothed he would join Marion and Sumter in marauding against the British posts to the south.

At last the new troops began to come in. Brigadier Generals John Butler and Thomas Eaton arrived with a thousand North Carolina militia. Brigadier General Robert Lawson brought in another thousand from Virginia. Also from Virginia, Steuben sent 530 Continentals.

In spite of desertions and the loss of Pickens's men, Nathanael now had more than 4200 soldiers. His scouts reported that Cornwallis had only between 2000 and 2300, though they were almost all disciplined veterans who could be relied upon in battle.

Less than 1500 of Nathanael's army were Continentals, the rest unreliable militia. But he could put off a battle no longer. The success or failure of his whole campaign in the South depended upon a final showdown with Cornwallis. And he had maneuvered the British commander into exactly the right position. He knew Cornwallis too wanted a battle. Well, he should have it, but where Nathanael wanted it—at Guilford Courthouse.

The British were camped about twelve miles to the south of it. Nathanael moved toward this battleground he had chosen so carefully while the army was retreating to the Dan. His main force was now closer to the enemy than it had been at any time before.

Cornwallis accepted the challenge. That night, March 14, while Light Horse Harry Lee's Legion was camped in the woods a few miles west of the main army, Lee was roused by an aide.

"A sentry reports the rumble of heavy wheels to the westward," the officer told him.

Lee was on his feet in an instant. "Cannon," he said.

"The whole British army must be on the move. Send a courier back to inform General Greene."

It was nearly noon now on this fifteenth day of March, 1781. Mounted on his horse, Nathanael halted beside the rude, deserted courthouse at the junction of two roads near the crest of the rise of ground on which his army was drawn up for battle.

He could see all of the battleground. What his thoughts were as he surveyed it and the three lines of waiting troops, no one knows. But his reading of the ancient philosophers had probably made him familiar with Plutarch's famous *Parallel Lives of Illustrious Greeks and Romans.* So he might have thought of Caesar's remark on the day of his assassination, another fifteenth of March eighteen centuries earlier: "The ides of March are come," and the soothsayer's ominous reply: "Yes, they are come, but they are not past."

Surely Nathanael, for all his boundless confidence in America's final victory in the Revolution, must have been beset by doubts that day. So much depended upon this battle . . . if he could only be sure those 2700 militia would stand firm against the first onslaught of the enemy . . .

Like every general, Nathanael had his faults. One was that he was too outspoken about his distrust of the militia. Of course, he was too good an officer ever to let his men hear him criticize them, but he did do so to others. Such things have a way of becoming known in an army. And men who know their leader does not trust them are less likely to be reliable when they face death.

It seemed a strange place for a courthouse, in this barren clearing, hemmed in on all sides by howling wilderness. The open space continued for perhaps 300 yards down the slope, which then became wooded and at last reached a valley through which ran Little Horsepen Creek. On this expanse, Nathanael could see no more than two or three farmhouses.

The main road from north to south ran down the middle of the clearing, bordered by cornfields; last year's stalks, bundled together in upright shocks, were like a ghostly army of straw men advancing over the rusty earth. Over this road Cornwallis must come.

Nathanael urged his horse forward and trotted down the slope. Toward its foot he reached the first of his three lines of defense, a formation much like the one Morgan had used at Cowpens. Mindful of the Old Wagoner's advice, he had placed the North Carolina militiamen in the center of this line, straddling the road. On their left were Lee's battle-hardened Legion and the sharpshooter mountaineer riflemen. To the militia's right were Colonel Washington's cavalry, more riflemen, and a battalion of light troops—Continentals from Delaware. Surely such firm supports on both sides of them should hearten the militiamen in the center, Nathanael reasoned.

He rode up and down the line of militia, his sword upraised for silence. "When the British come, give them two rounds, boys," he said, as Morgan had at Cowpens. "Just two rounds, and then you may fall back."

He wheeled his mount and rode up the slope to the second line, about 300 yards behind. It was shorter than the first, for it was composed only of Virginia militia, without the support the first one had on its flanks. But the Virginians were more experienced than the North Carolina men. Among them too was a scattering of Continentals whose enlistments had expired, and who had been hired by faint-hearted militiamen to return to the army as their substitutes.

*118*

This was the line upon which Nathanael must rely to bear the brunt of the attack once the militia in the first one had retired. Just behind it he had stationed 40 picked marksmen.

He rode up to Brigadier General Edward Stevens, in command of the brigade on the right of the line. "Have you informed the men that the marksmen behind them have orders to shoot them down if they run without orders to fall back?" he asked.

At the battle of Camden, Stevens's militia had humiliated him by fleeing, scarcely firing a shot. Now he said grimly, "They know it, sir." A similar answer came from Brigadier General Lawson, commanding the left of the line, across the road.

Then Nathanael rode back to his post near the courthouse, from which he could direct the battle and rally the troops if they did retreat in disorder. He passed his third line, about 500 yards behind the second, without stopping. They needed no advice. They were the crack troops, dependable, cool and unafraid in action—the Virginia Continentals under General Huger on the right, Otho Williams's seasoned Maryland fighters on the left.

With his two mounted aides at his side, Nathanael kept his eyes fixed on the first line, far down the slope. He sensed their nervousness. He hoped the enemy would soon appear; the longer the wait the worse it was going to be for those militia.

Suddenly one of the two cannon he had placed in the center of the first line erupted in flame and smoke, followed instantly by the second. Nathanael raised himself in his stirrups, peering down where the road disappeared into the wooded valley below.

Yes!—they were coming. He could see the van of the enemy column spreading out as it deployed. The crossed white belts of the British Regulars stood out sharply against the brilliant scarlet of their coats. There too were the blue of Hessian uniforms, the green of the yagers. Burnished muskets and fixed bayonets flashed menacingly in the sunlight of the cloudless sky.

There was an implacable deadliness in the way the enemy came on. Cornwallis could depend upon them to be unflinching. Yet Nathanael, anxiously scanning his first line, knew that what the British and Hessians saw must be equally terror-inspiring. The drably clad militia in the center were ranged behind a tumbledown rail fence. Their muskets were steadied on the top rails. The advancing enemy would see a long row of uncompromising black muzzles, ready to spew death.

The commanders of the two North Carolina brigades had raised their swords. Then came the first volley, an uneven rattle rather than a single roar, yet it tore gaping holes in the British ranks. In a flash, Nathanael saw that another such blast would break their line. *Just one more,* he prayed.

The enemy had halted. Nathanael could hear the barked commands of their officers and the businesslike thud of the ramrods as the soldiers loaded. Then came the crash of their volley.

The opposing lines almost disappeared in the smoke, but a British order to charge with the bayonet and the soldiers' yell as they swept forward came clearly through it. Nathanael waited tensely for the second American volley.

He uttered a stricken cry as the smoke began to lift. The militia had broken in the face of that oncoming phalanx of glittering steel. A few of them fired again; then they too joined the others in dashing helter-skelter to the rear, throwing away their guns as they ran.

Perhaps because the fleeing militiamen knew the sharp-shooters were just behind the center of the second line, they headed for its flanks. If they had plunged straight into it, the second line too would have been thrown into confusion.

General Leslie, commanding the British advance, sent part of his force wheeling to the right toward Lee's cavalry. It cut the American horsemen off from the battle.

The rest of the British moved toward the Virginia militia of the second line. Nathanael knew that if it broke quickly, like the first, the fight would surely be lost. But for a time it stood firm, returning the British fire, volley for volley.

At last its right side wavered. It did not break, but fell back slowly. On its right flank were Colonel Washington's cavalry and the light troops, which had retired to the second line when the militia of the first fled. They swarmed in to stem the enemy advance, but were repulsed and forced back toward the third line.

The left side of the second line was still holding, but now the right wing collapsed and ran. Through this gaping hole, the British regiments and the Hessian yagers burst in a charge straight for the third line.

The Continentals were ready for them. The whole line of this last bulwark exploded in a crashing volley. Along the front of the British advance, men fell like a pushed-over stack of dominoes. Instantly Colonel John Gunby of the Maryland Continentals seized the opportunity. He ordered a countercharge with the bayonet. The enemy was driven back.

Nathanael, who was now only a short distance in the rear of the fighting, saw that a countercharge by the entire Continental line might rout the whole British army.

*121*

But he saw too that if it failed his own army might be destroyed. For a moment he weighed one chance against the other, then decided on caution. He had too much to lose by risking the countercharge.

Now the left side of the second line began to crumble. Gradually it was forced back past the courthouse and into the woods northwest of it. With that, the British who had thrust them back wheeled in upon the Continentals. They struck at a Maryland regiment which had not been in battle before.

The Maryland men broke and ran. On the other end of the line, Colonel Washington saw their flight. He took his cavalry in a wide sweep behind the Continentals and fell upon the British attackers, riding over them and cutting many down. Then Gunby's Maryland regiment and the light troops who had retired from the first line swarmed in and drove the enemy advance back.

The center of the British line was disintegrating before the Continentals' fire. Other redcoats came in from the right just in time to keep them from fleeing. But they too were staggered by the ferocity of the American fire and began to fall back.

There was hand-to-hand fighting and so much confusion in the smoke-filled clearing that Nathanael spurred his horse and rode into the thick of the battle, encouraging his men. Once only a warning shout from one of his aides kept him from being captured when he was almost surrounded by the enemy.

Now a magnificent figure in scarlet, white, and gold rode into the clearing on his charger. From his post in the rear, Cornwallis had seen he was needed, with his army near defeat.

He ordered three cannon into the southwest corner of the clearing to fire grapeshot into the melee on the crest of the rise. One of his officers pleaded with him not to, for the bursting shells, with their death-dealing contents of cast iron balls, would mow down British as well as Americans. But Cornwallis, knowing he must thrust the enemy back to save his own army from its desperate situation, paid no heed.

The cannon fire forced the Continentals back. Officers of both armies struggled to reform ranks. On the British side, Cornwallis demanded one more attack.

Again Nathanael was forced to a decision. Should he try to stop it? The battle had been raging more than two hours and the men were exhausted. The Americans had had to abandon their four cannon when the horses used to move them were shot. And Nathanael knew he had achieved a devastating blow against Cornwallis's army, as good as a victory.

He ordered a retreat. Tarleton's dragoons tried to pursue, but the Continentals, falling back slowly, repulsed them with unerring marksmanship.

The British had won the battle of Guilford Courthouse, but at a terrible cost. Cornwallis had lost more than a fourth of his army in killed and wounded. The American casualties were only about half as great. The English statesman, Charles James Fox, said when he learned of the battle, "Another such victory would destroy the British army."

He also said, "America is irretrievably lost to this country." How right he was about that will soon be seen.

# 11 ★★★★★★★★★★★★★★★★★★

*We fight, get beat, rise and fight again.* NATHANAEL GREENE

Nathanael was exhausted by the strain of the long retreat, the days of maneuvering to bring Cornwallis to battle, the fight itself, and especially the tremendous responsibility he had borne for the army's safety. He fainted the night after the battle and again the next night, but he refused to take it seriously. As soon as he could he wrote to Kitty, telling her about the fight. "Our fatigue has been excessive," he added, "but I am generally in pretty good health."

He yearned to see her and the children. "I should be extremely happy if the war had an honorable close," he wrote, "and I on a farm with my little family about me. God grant the day may not be far distant when peace, with all her train of blessings, shall diffuse universal joy throughout America."

It would be many months before his wish came true, yet when Cornwallis left the field at Guilford Courthouse he began a march that would finally end at Yorktown.

Nathanael was amused when Cornwallis sent an officer to the American camp under a flag of truce with a pompous message. "His Lordship, General Cornwallis, reminds you, sir, that he has driven you from the battlefield with the loss of all your cannon," the emissary said, "and that you now have no recourse but to surrender."

Nathanael managed to keep his expression sober. Recalling what he had written to a friend after the equally disastrous British victory at Bunker Hill, he replied, "Pray give his Lordship my compliments, and say that I shall be glad to sell him another field at the same price."

For three days both armies rested their men, cared for the wounded, and buried the dead. Then, on March 18, Nathanael's scouts reported that the British had marched, headed southeast.

"Lord Cornwallis appears to be making for his base on the coast at Wilmington," Nathanael told his officers. "Since we did not quite finish what we started at Guilford Courthouse, we will march after the enemy and try to force him to another battle."

Now Cornwallis was the fox, though a gaunt and scarred one, and the Americans the hounds. But the British commander had one advantage in marching ahead. His foraging parties swept the countryside so clear of food that Nathanael's army could obtain almost nothing to eat. The famished men grew so weak that many fell fainting in the road and had to be carried in the already overloaded wagons.

Light Horse Harry Lee unwittingly solved the problem temporarily. Nathanael had sent his Legion ahead to hang on the enemy's heels and try to impede his progress. Lee's swift horsemen overtook Cornwallis at Ramsey's Mill on the Deep River.

The British sentinels sounded the alarm and Cornwallis, thinking it might be the whole American army, got his troops out so fast that a bridge they had built over the river was left standing, and a store of meat abandoned. When Nathanael's men arrived, they fell voraciously on whole quarters of beef left hanging in the slaughtering pens. Some, arriving too late, devoured garbage the British had thrown out.

At Ramsey's Mill, Nathanael called his officers together. "The country ahead is pine barrens with few habitations," he said. "If we pursue the enemy farther, we shall be obliged to collect a store of provisions first. Since the British have already plundered the neighborhood, this would delay us and give us little chance of catching up. I have therefore decided to abandon the pursuit and march into South Carolina."

He spread out a map, and with the officers gathered around, his finger moved southwestward from the camp. "Our first objective will be Camden."

There were murmurs of approval from those who had fought in the battle there under General Gates. They wanted nothing so much as revenge for that disaster. Others shook their heads dubiously.

"Cornwallis got into trouble when he marched too far from his bases of supply," said one. "We will be at the same disadvantage if we move too far from our Virginia base."

"There is a difference," said Nathanael. "The British strongholds in South Carolina are well stocked with food, clothing, arms, and ammunition. If we can capture these posts, the supplies will fall to us."

"The militia from Virginia and North Carolina are going home," another officer objected. "Their time is up. It will leave us with no more than two or three hundred militia."

"We have over a thousand Continentals," Nathanael reminded him. "I am writing Baron von Steuben in Virginia to send us 500 more Virginia militia. I believe others will join us as we march south."

To Lee, he said, "Your Legion will ride to the Pee Dee River and join General Marion there. You will prevent reinforcements reaching the British at Camden from their base at Charleston."

Nathanael's plan was for the main army to strike at some of the important British strongholds in South Carolina as the first move to recapture control of that state. Meanwhile, he would depend upon Marion and Pickens to move against the smaller posts.

It was unlikely that Cornwallis would turn and pursue again with his weakened army. Nor did the possibility worry Nathanael. He was confident that if the British leader did do so, he would be destroyed.

On April 6 the march began. At first the way led through a desolate region of pine barrens, threaded by several good-sized rivers and countless creeks, all bordered by dismal swamps where gray Spanish moss festooned the trees. But spring had come, the army was deep in the South, and the weather was warm. Ahead of them lay rich farmlands where an advance party of foragers was collecting an ample store of food.

On April 19, after marching over a hundred miles, the army camped on Hobkirk's Hill, a long, sandy ridge, thickly covered with trees. Below it, a mile and a half away, lay Camden on a plain along the Wateree River and surrounded on all sides by dense pine forests.

Nathanael saw at a glance that its position was strong. On two sides it was bordered by the Wateree and a smaller stream, Pine Tree Creek. Its other sides were protected by a chain of redoubts, with a stockade at the center. It would have to be besieged, since the American cannon were not heavy enough to batter down the defenses.

There on Hobkirk's Hill, Nathanael waited hopefully for several days. He had sent word to Thomas Sumter asking him to come with his corps and join the army. But the temperamental Gamecock was still smarting over the fancied slight he had received by Morgan's appointment. He did not come.

Lord Francis Rawdon, the young colonel in command of the garrison at Camden, was said to be the ugliest man in the British army, but his ability in battle was handsome indeed, as he had proved at Bunker Hill and in other fights. Soon after the Americans camped on Hobkirk's Hill, a deserter made his way to Camden and told Rawdon that Nathanael's army was weak, almost starved and could not fight a battle because Sumter had not brought up his reinforcements.

Rawdon knew he could not withstand a siege for long. He had only about 900 men and his provisions were low. But if he could catch the enemy by surprise he might destroy them.

On the morning of April 25, while the Americans were having their breakfasts, the sentinels on the outposts sounded the alarm by firing their muskets. Nathanael, who was dining in his tent, leaped up and summoned Captain Robert Kirkwood, commanding the light infantry. "Take your men to the picket lines to delay the enemy!" he shouted.

Luckily, he had ordered the army to encamp in the battle formation he intended to use in case of just such an attack. The men were quickly made ready to fight.

Peering down the slope of the ridge through the trees, Nathanael could see Kirkwood's men falling back slowly before the enemy. Rawdon's men were advancing in a single line. He realized that this gave him a chance for a quick, complete victory.

"We'll strike them from four directions at once," he told his officers. He ordered the Continental regiments on the far right and left of his line to wheel in on the enemy's flanks. Colonel Washington was sent with his cavalry to circle through the woods and come at the British from the rear.

128

Nathanael had obtained two cannon to replace those captured at Guilford Courthouse. He placed them in the middle of the line and ordered them to open fire. Then he sent the Continental regiments in the center directly at the oncoming redcoats in a bayonet charge. Taking no chances with his militia this time, he stationed the 250 North Carolina men in the rear as a reserve.

With a blast of cannon fire and roar of musketry, the battle began. Nathanael, riding up and down behind his advancing center line, saw that everything was going as he had hoped. The artillery, loaded with grapeshot, was tearing wide gaps in the British center. His own center was advancing steadily.

But he knew he was meeting an experienced, clever fighter. Rawdon would make no mistakes. Already he had met the challenge to his flanks by extending his line outward. In spite of the withering cannon fire, his center was holding firm.

Suddenly Nathanael stiffened on his mount. What was wrong there in the center? Something had thrown three companies of a Maryland Continental regiment into disorder. Yet their line was not broken; a strong hand would restore their formation.

The strong hand was there, Nathanael felt sure. Their commander, Colonel Gunby, was a brilliant, courageous officer. At Guilford Courthouse he had led the charge that had almost routed the British. He was shouting at his men, but his words were lost in the din of the fight. Thus Nathanael could not believe what he saw when the Maryland men began to fall back.

A great shout went up from the redcoats who were facing them. Again Lord Rawdon had been quick to see what was needed. He had ordered them to charge Gunby's retreating regiment. The Maryland men were running now, scrambling frantically over the top of the ridge.

The Virginia Continentals in the center were still advancing. They might yet prevent a rout. Nathanael galloped up, shouting encouragement. Then, to his consternation, he saw that some of these regiments too were beginning to turn back, fleeing up the slope.

Only Lieutenant Colonel Samuel Hawes's regiment remained in line. His men were covering the retreating troops magnificently, holding off the enemy. But Nathanael saw that they would inevitably be surrounded. He ordered them back.

The battle was lost. Now the cannon were in danger of being captured. The artillerymen were trying desperately to drag the guns up the slope, through the tangle of underbrush. Nathanael rode up, dismounted, and joined them, seizing one of the drag ropes himself.

A party of Rawdon's cavalry dashed in on the cannon. But just then Colonel Washington's cavalry, returning from the British rear, charged in, scattering the enemy riders. Then horses were brought up from the American rear and the guns hauled to safety. Nathanael rode back to collect his scattered army. He and his officers managed to halt and assemble the men three miles from Hobkirk's Hill.

Unlike the battle of Guilford Courthouse, this defeat could not be called a victory in its effects. The American army had been soundly beaten. It had lost 250 precious troops in killed, wounded and missing. And the battle had done nothing toward achieving Nathanael's objectives.

Yet he doggedly refused to let it dishearten him. In a letter to Baron von Steuben, he said, "This repulse, if repulse it may be called, will make no alteration in our general plan of operations."

To the French ambassador to the United States, the Chevalier de la Luzerne, with whom he had become well acquainted in Philadelphia, he wrote, "We fight, get beat, rise and fight again."

★ ★ ★ ★ ★ ★ ★ ★ ★ ★ ★ ★ ★ ★ ★ ★ ★

*Fortune may have yet a better success in
reserve for you, and they who lose to-day
may win to-morrow.* MIGUEL DE CERVANTES

Nathanael was inclined to blame Colonel Gunby for
the defeat at Hobkirk's Hill. Indeed, if Gunby had not
ordered the Maryland regiments to fall back, the Americans would probably have scored a decisive victory.

Gunby insisted it had been necessary to withdraw his
men to restore their ranks to order. A court of inquiry
decided that although he had shown great bravery in the
battle, he should not have given the order, and that this
had caused the defeat.

One piece of good news reached the camp. Lee and
Marion had captured Fort Watson, one of the strongest of
the smaller British posts in South Carolina. The victory
was especially important because the fort stood on
Rawdon's line of communication with his supply base at
Charleston.

Nathanael took his army a few miles back for a rest at
Rugeley's Mill. His prospects for carrying on the campaign were discouraging. The countryside was barren and
gave no promise of providing food. The warning sounded
by one of his officers that he might find himself in the
same trouble as Cornwallis if he marched too far south
must have been much in his mind.

He wrote to Thomas Sumter, who was with his corps in

the region to the south, around Orangeburg. "My great dependence will be on you for supplies of corn and meal. Both of these articles are immediately wanted, and unless you can furnish me with them it will be impossible for me to keep my position here."

On May 3 Nathanael moved his army southwestward across the Wateree in the hope of finding food. He was greatly worried, for he had learned that 500 British Regulars were on their way to join Rawdon at Camden. Another attack by the strengthened British garrison might finish his own army.

More bad news came. Lee and Marion had tried to intercept the enemy reinforcements, but were too late. On May 7 the 500 redcoats joined Lord Rawdon.

But Rawdon was in trouble too. He had more men, but no provisions for them, since his stock of food was almost exhausted. Not only did the loss of Fort Watson imperil his chances of getting supplies from Charleston, but so did Nathanael's army and the forces of Lee and Marion, all planted across the route.

On May 10 Rawdon marched his garrison out of Camden after burning everything in the camp the Americans could possibly use. He headed southeast for the region beyond the Santee River. Nathanael had lost a battle but had gained Britain's chief stronghold in central South Carolina. He marched in and took possession of it.

The luck had changed. First, Lee and Marion, carrying out Nathanael's orders, laid siege to another of the smaller British outposts, Fort Motte, about 40 miles south of Camden. It surrendered after a few days.

The army's hunger was relieved too. Sumter sent the corn and meal Nathanael asked for, though he still made no move to obey the order to join the main army with his corps. The Gamecock had his own plans, and wanted no one to tell him what to do. With his partisans, he attacked the strong British fort at Orangeburg and took it.

Then some of Pickens's and Sumter's men captured two British couriers. They were carrying messages from Lord Rawdon to the commanders of two other British outposts —one at Fort Granby, 30 miles southwest of Camden, the other at Ninety-Six, nearly a hundred miles west. They were ordered to abandon the posts and join Rawdon. The partisan commanders sent the dispatches to Nathanael.

He read them with satisfaction. Now he was feeling better.

"We'll let those garrisons stay right where they are and try to capture them," he said. "I'll send Lee against Fort Granby. We will march for Ninety-Six."

He wanted to talk to Lee and Marion. Leaving the army to start westward under General Huger, he rode south with a small escort of cavalry to Fort Motte.

It was merely a house surrounded by a palisade and a ditch. There, for the first time, Nathanael met the man whose daring and resourcefulness had been a fortress of strength in the southern campaign.

He greeted Francis Marion with a warmth that showed his gratitude. From Marion's deeds and the letters which had constantly passed between them, Nathanael already knew his character and military ability. Yet he gazed at the Swamp Fox with great curiosity.

Marion was neither handsome nor impressive. At first glance it seemed incredible that this middle-aged, small, slender man could be such a terror to the British. Marion's cold, impassive face and his moody look told Nathanael that here was a man who had few close friends. Yet the partisan leader's eyes burned with a feverish light that revealed his intense patriotism. Nor did Nathanael miss the doglike devotion in the eyes of his roughly dressed men with the white cockades in their hats.

Marion spoke of how Fort Watson had been captured: "It was a strong fortification. We could not have taken it but for the Maham Tower."

"Tower?" Nathanael repeated.

"A tower devised by Colonel Maham from which our riflemen could fire down upon the enemy inside the fort, General."

"Have him fetched here," said Nathanael. "I want to know more about this."

Colonel Hezekiah Maham told how the tower had been built of logs piled in a rectangular structure 40 feet high, with a platform on top for the sharpshooters.

"Whence came this idea of yours?" Nathanael wanted to know.

"From my reading of history, sir. It is like the siege towers used in ancient days."

Nathanael was delighted. Here was a man who, like himself, had read the writers of antiquity and profited by it.

He spoke to Marion: "You will watch Lord Rawdon's movements while Colonel Lee strikes at Fort Granby. I am worried lest Rawdon may turn and follow us toward Ninety-Six, once he learns his order to abandon the fort there never reached its commander."

Then he and his escort set off to rejoin the main army. Lee marched his Legion at once to attack Fort Granby. It was well fortified, but although its commander had 350 men and five heavy guns, it surrendered after Light Horse Harry Lee sent a few cannon balls crashing into the walls at close range.

Except for the British bases on the coast at Charleston

and Georgetown, only one enemy post now remained in South Carolina—Ninety-Six. One other must also be taken before British control of the state was broken—Augusta, on the Savannah River, just across the Georgia border. Andrew Pickens was already besieging it.

With Fort Granby taken, Nathanael sent Lee to join Pickens. Now for Ninety-Six . . .

Meanwhile, news of the army's prowess spread quickly. From his headquarters on the Hudson, Washington sent a general order congratulating Nathanael and his men. "These brilliant repeated successes which reflect so much glory on the Southern Army will be attended with the most important consequences," it said. Nathanael's friend and correspondent, Joseph Reed of the Continental Congress wrote from Philadelphia: "You have won the admiration of the whole country. People say that if Greene cannot preserve the country, it is because it cannot be preserved."

Nathanael was now hopeful over his prospects. So vigilant were Pickens's scouts in the country to the west that they intercepted all messages from Lord Rawdon to the British commander at Ninety-Six. There was no indication in them that Rawdon planned to march to his rescue.

On May 22 the army reached Ninety-Six. Its odd name was due to its establishment during the Indian wars as a fortified stopping place on the old trail from Charleston to the western mountains. It was 96 miles from the nearest of the forts which had been built on the frontier against Indian attacks.

With one of his aides and the Polish engineer, Colonel Kosciusko, Nathanael reconnoitered the enemy's position. They saw at a glance that capturing Ninety-Six was not going to be easy, for the British had strengthened its defenses immensely. A stout wooden palisade surrounded the little village, and it was protected by two very strong fortifications, one on the east, the other on the west.

On the east, just outside the palisade, was a star-shaped earthen redoubt with sixteen points or salients; on the west a strong stockade fort. Each was surrounded by a deep ditch, an abatis of felled trees with their branches sharpened, and a latticework of sharpened stakes known as a cheval-de-frise.

The stockade fort was about 180 yards from the village. Between the two a covered way—a path protected by a covering of planks—traversed a ravine. The officers' attention fell upon this ravine, for in it was a spring upon which the garrison depended for its water.

"It may be a fatal weakness," said Nathanael. "If we can cut off the water supply, the enemy will be in desperate straits."

"That will not be easy," said Kosciusko, pointing to an old jail just inside the village which had been converted into a sort of citadel, towering above the palisade. "The ravine is covered by the guns there, as well as those of the stockade fort. But by constructing parallels, we can approach close enough to keep the place under a tight siege and perhaps cut off the water supply."

Nathanael called a war council. "We will lay siege to the place," he announced.

"Why not an assault, General?" someone asked. "We have over a thousand men, most of them Continentals. The enemy garrison cannot be large."

"Our intelligence indicates there are about 600 Loyalist troops, 350 of them Regulars," Nathanael replied. "Their commander, Lieutenant Colonel Cruger, is also a Tory and a very capable officer. Colonel Kosciusko agrees with me that an assault would be most difficult and likely to cost us very severe casualties."

He told them of the plan to dig parallels—trenches running parallel to the fortifications to prevent the enemy from blasting them with fire down their length. When one parallel was completed, a connecting trench would be dug at an angle, under cover of earthworks, and a second, nearer parallel begun. Thus, in a series of zigzag trenches, an attacking force could be brought close to the enemy.

"We will divide the army into four sections, camped to the northeast, southeast, southwest, and northwest to cut off the enemy's communications so that help cannot be summoned," he said.

"Suppose Cruger sallies out with all his force," an officer objected. "He could fall upon one of our camps and destroy it."

"I don't think he will risk it," Nathanael replied. "It would give the other three sections of our army a chance to rush the fortifications and capture them."

The siege began. All through that night a horde of soldiers, burrowing furiously, worked on the first parallel, within 200 feet of the star-shaped fort. When morning came they were well protected by the mountain of earth they had thrown up, and the work could proceed by day.

But not for long. A detachment of Tory soldiers rushed out of the fort with fixed bayonets and cut the working party almost to pieces. Nathanael had to order a new parallel begun at a safer distance while he worked out plans to prevent such assaults.

It took them a week to reach the place where the first parallel had been started. Almost every night there were fierce attacks by enemy parties which stole out in the darkness. Colonel Cruger and his Tories were tough opponents. Nathanael tried a number of measures against these attacks, but each was met by an enemy counter-measure.

One night the wind rose to a gale. Nathanael summoned one of his captains. "Send out a party of ten men to sneak up on the stockade fort and set fire to the walls," he ordered. "In this storm the flames will spread rapidly."

Alert Tory sentinels saw the men creeping toward the fort. An enemy detachment met them and killed all but four.

"We'll build a Maham Tower near the star fort," Nathanael decided. When it was done and marksmen posted on its top, any enemy soldier who dared show his head above the walls was a dead man. In retaliation, Cruger ordered red-hot shot fired at the tower, but it was made of green wood which did not ignite. Then he had the walls of the fort raised by piling sandbags on them. That gave his men more protection.

"Our tower won't burn," said Nathanael, "but the houses in the village will. Have the cannon fire red-hot balls at the rooftops." But Cruger had the roofs removed from the houses.

Meanwhile, Marion, Pickens, and Light Horse Harry Lee were not idle. The Swamp Fox attacked the British coastal base of Georgetown and captured it. Lee and Pickens assaulted and took Augusta. Then Lee took his Legion and the prisoners to join Nathanael at Ninety-Six.

In spite of all this good news, Nathanael was uneasy. His worst fears were realized when he learned that 2000 British troops had landed at Charleston from Ireland, and that Rawdon was marching with them for Ninety-Six.

He sent out couriers with orders to Sumter and Marion to do all they could to delay Rawdon. He also sent Pickens and Washington's cavalry over the road toward

Charleston with the same instructions. Then he summoned Kosciusko.

"How are the parallels progressing?" he asked.

"We are within a few feet of the fort's walls," was the answer. "Give us a few days and we'll drive a tunnel under the works. With a few barrels of powder we can blast a breach in the walls big enough for the army to rush inside."

A few days . . . Nathanael hesitated. One thing he felt sure of: Cruger knew nothing of Rawdon's coming. Parallels had also been dug on the other side of the village, close to the ravine. The enemy no longer dared to go there by daylight, and sent Negro slaves to the spring at night, hoping they could not be seen in the darkness. The enemy might yet conclude it was hopeless to hold out any longer. Nathanael decided to wait a day or two before his next move.

Then, on June 17, a rider in countryman's dress trotted over the road leading through the southward American positions to the main gate in the village walls. The sentries let him pass. People often came into the camp, curious to see what was going on.

Suddenly the rider dug his heels into his horse's sides and was off like a shot toward the gate. A storm of bullets whistled about his ears, but he reached it and was admitted. Now Colonel Cruger knew help was coming.

Hastily, Nathanael summoned his officers. "We can wait no longer for the tunnel to be completed," he said. "Once Rawdon arrives, we are lost. Since Cruger knows he is coming, he will not surrender. We must assault the enemy's works."

"The men are all for it," said Lee. "You might take the place by a mass assault, General, but in my opinion you'll lose at least 200 men."

Nathanael shook his head. "With Lord Rawdon approaching, we can't take that risk. We'll send a picked force of volunteers against the works."

Lee agreed to attack the stockade fort with his Legion, supported by a detachment of Delaware Continental volunteers. Such a force was known to military men as a forlorn hope because its chances of survival were small. A similar forlorn hope of Maryland and Virginia Continentals was to make the assault against the star fort.

On the morning of June 18, all was ready. Marksmen on the Maham Tower were ready to cover the attack on the star fort with rifle fire. In the parallels, in addition to men armed with muskets, some of the forlorn hope carried axes, some bundles of brushwood tied together and known as fascines, others iron hooks.

Nathanael gave the officers of the two forces final instructions. His orders to Lee were simple: "You must storm the stockade fort, get inside and take it, Colonel."

To Lieutenants Isaac Duval and Samuel Seldon, leaders of the forlorn hope that was to go against the star fort, he said, "Once the axemen have cut away the abatis, those with fascines will pile them in the ditch. The hookmen will stand on them, reach up, and pull down the sandbags, piling them on top of the fascines. In that way your men will be able to scale the walls."

It was eleven o'clock when a cannon was fired as a signal to begin the assault. The axemen leaped from the trenches and hurled themselves toward the ditch. Nathanael, watching from an elevated cannon emplacement, saw them almost disappear in a cloud of smoke that billowed and boiled from the muskets of the defenders on the parapet. But he could hear the steady clunk of their axes intermingled with the blast of the guns.

A yell from the axemen revealed that they had cut away

*141*

the abatis. Another wave of the forlorn hope surged toward the ditch, throwing down their fascines. Then came the hookmen and the rest of the troops.

Even by standing on the piled-up fascines, the hookmen could scarcely reach the sandbags on top of the parapet. Many men were shot down by musket fire and impaled by the bayonets and long, sharp-pointed pikes thrust down at them by the Tories above. Nevertheless, the defenders had to expose themselves, and the riflemen in the Maham Tower were picking them off.

A messenger dashed in from the other side of the village. The Legion and the Delaware Continentals had fought their way inside the stockade fort.

All now depended upon the star-fort assault. As nearly as Nathanael could tell, it was succeeding. More and more sandbags were being pulled down. The men of the forlorn hope would soon be able to pull themselves up and over the parapet.

Then a groan escaped Nathanael. Cruger had sent a detachment from the fort into the ditch, their bayonets fixed. The action there became a confused melee of hand-to-hand fighting. Bodies of the dead and wounded were added to the growing pile of sandbags.

Once more Nathanael faced a critical decision. He saw that if he launched another company of Continentals into the ditch it would probably tip the balance in favor of the Americans. But his losses were already severe. Could he take the chance of losing more men, with Lord Rawdon's reinforcements so near?

Again, prudence overcame Nathanael's impulse to risk all for the sake of a sweeping victory. "Have the troops retire from the ditch," he ordered. "Send word to Lee to abandon the stockade fort."

The men in the ditch were brought off in spite of a murderous fire from the parapet, taking most of the wounded with them. The Americans had lost about 150 in killed, wounded, and missing; the Tory defenders only half as many.

At a hastily summoned council, one of Nathanael's officers felt the army's situation, with Rawdon approaching, was desperate. "We must fall back to Virginia," he said.

"No," replied Nathanael. "We will retreat, but not to Virginia. I will recover South Carolina or die in the attempt. Rawdon cannot hold Ninety-Six for long, with our partisans cutting off his communications with Charleston."

It proved wise counsel. The American army fell back to the northeast. A day later, Lord Rawdon arrived at Ninety-Six. He too saw that it was impossible to hold it, with all the other British posts in the region gone.

Leaving Colonel Cruger with 1400 men to destroy the fortifications, Rawdon marched away with the rest of his force, 1200 men. He headed southeast, toward Charleston. When word that he had divided his army reached the Americans, they turned about and marched south in pursuit of the weaker of the two enemy forces.

Nathanael had lost another battle. Of all those he took part in, it would have been better if this one of Ninety-Six had never been fought. Since he knew beforehand that the British were planning to abandon it, his only purpose in besieging it was to capture or destroy the enemy garrison. He did neither, and in the assault he lost twice as many men as Cruger did.

A more daring general, willing to take the risk of losing his whole army, might have won. But such a general would probably already have fallen a victim to Cornwallis in the long retreat. Prudence and caution were the cornerstones of Nathanael's campaign in the South.

*The more he is beaten, the farther he advances
in the end.* LIEUTENANT FREDERICK MACKENZIE

It was early summer now, and in South Carolina the
weather was insufferably hot. The sweating, dog-tired
army was pestered by hordes of mosquitoes and tiny,
stinging gnats as it plodded in pursuit of the enemy.

The Americans finally caught up with Rawdon at
Orangeburg. Nathanael saw that an assault on the town
would be hopeless. His cannon could do nothing against
the thick-walled brick prison the enemy was using as a
fortress. He camped outside the town for a few days,
hoping the British might come out and fight. But Lord
Rawdon was too smart an officer to do that against a
much superior force, for at last Sumter had joined the
main army, along with Marion, bringing in a thousand
additional troops.

Nathanael now decided to retire to a camp which
would be safe from surprise, give his men a real rest and
strengthen his army further before moving against the
British again. He sent Sumter, Marion, and most of Lee's
and Washington's cavalry to attack enemy outposts
around Charleston. Then the main army marched northeast about 30 miles and halted.

The camp was on the High Hills of the Santee, a long
chain of red sand hills rising about 200 feet above the
Wateree River. Not only their elevation, but an impenetrable swamp three or four miles wide along the riverbank

144

protected the army. To the east, the country was fertile farmland, promising an excellent supply of food. The hills were cooler than the bottomlands below, and there were fewer insects to torment the soldiers.

While his men enjoyed their well-earned rest and better food than they had seen in many weeks, Nathanael was able to catch up on neglected correspondence. He had written Kitty as often as possible, but now the letters were longer and more frequent.

To his old friend Henry Knox too, he wrote at length about his adventures. Major John Trumbull, Washington's secretary, had said Nathanael was deficient in the art of retreating. Perhaps he was so stung by the criticism that he forgot his grammar, for he wrote to Knox: "There are few generals that has run oftener, or more lustily than I have done. But I have taken care not to run too far, and commonly have run as fast forward as backward, to convince our Enemy that we were like a Crab, that could run either way."

He continued to keep General Washington informed of all that happened. He also wrote to Lafayette, Steuben, and his old friend, Daniel Morgan. To Joseph Reed and to Robert Morris, now head of the government's financial department, he sent urgent appeals for more support, and especially much-needed cash.

Meanwhile, Nathanael saw to it that his men were drilled constantly and well disciplined. He was in close touch with Lee and Marion, who were watching the British. Lord Rawdon, who had fallen seriously ill and returned to England, had been replaced by Colonel Alexander Stewart.

The American army remained on the High Hills of the Santee for six weeks. Then, on August 17, Lee wrote Nathanael about Cornwallis's intentions. "I am of the

145

opinion . . . that his Lordship will shortly be in Charleston," he said. "It would be great to strike Stewart before his friend arrives."

Nathanael was greatly disturbed. It had been raining for days. He had only to look out over the bottomlands below the camp to see that his army could never cross the Wateree there to meet Stewart's force, which had marched south from Orangeburg to a point a little below where the Wateree and Congaree united to form the Santee River. The swollen Wateree had turned the swamp along its banks into a vast lake, and flooded the surrounding countryside.

Yet march the American army must. If Lee were correct, and Cornwallis joined Stewart, South Carolina might well fall into British hands again. Stewart's army must be met and defeated before that could happen.

Studying his maps, Nathanael planned a roundabout route of march to avoid the inundated region. He sent Lee orders to meet the main army at Howell's Ferry, where it would cross the Congaree. "Depend upon it," he added, "we must have victory or ruin."

He also sent express riders to bring Marion and Pickens in with their troops. Then, on August 23, the army marched. It made a 70-mile detour, slogging north through the mud to Camden, crossing the Wateree there, then swinging south again, headed for the Congaree.

While the army was camped on the High Hills, lavish promises of reinforcements had come from the governors of Virginia, North Carolina, and South Carolina, but only about 400 militia and a regiment of Continentals ever arrived. Nevertheless, with Pickens's and Marion's corps, Nathanael now had about 2500 men, including 1250 Continentals. His intelligence reports showed Stewart to have about 2300 Regulars. If the two armies met they would be well matched.

Colonel Stewart had moved farther down the Santee River. There he hoped reinforcements and supplies would reach him from Charleston.

The British camp was at Eutaw Springs, set among tall pines along Eutaw Creek on a road which ran toward Charleston. Just above it, two springs bubbled up from the sandy soil to form the little winding stream which flowed into the Santee two miles beyond. Eutaw Springs was a tiny hamlet, but it did boast Eutaw House, a stoutly-built mansion of brick, three stories high, with extensive gardens around it.

Lee and his Legion met Nathanael's army when it crossed the Congaree and began the last leg of its march. It moved slowly and cautiously, for he wanted to surprise Stewart if possible; also, the heat of the southern sun was ferocious, and he could not risk exhausting the men.

There was no meat to feed them, for the commissary's store of beef was used up. But the gloomy swamps which edged the Charleston road abounded in giant bullfrogs. Their fat legs, when broiled, were tasty morsels. Some of the soldiers even shot alligators, and since hunger is good sauce, no doubt they found steaks cut from the scaly monsters quite palatable.

On September 7 the army reached a plantation only seven miles from the enemy's camp. Here Francis Marion and his men arrived. Pickens had already come in, as had a detachment sent by Sumter.

Nathanael was up long before dawn the next morning, and it was only four when the army marched in two main columns. As he had done at Guilford Courthouse, he assigned his militia to the first line of attack—two North Carolina and two South Carolina battalions in the center. Since they had been well drilled and disciplined on the High Hills, Nathanael was hopeful that they would hold firm, at least for a time. And they would be flanked by

Marion's reliable fighters on the right and those of Pickens on the left.

The second line was all Continentals. Its weakest part would be the right, for here the soldiers, from North Carolina, were inexperienced in battle. In the center would be the trusty Virginians, and on the left the best troops of all—the Maryland men under Otho Williams.

Lee's Legion and the detachment of Sumter's men formed the advance as the army marched. In the rear came Colonel Washington's cavalry and the redoubtable Delaware Continentals. In the center of each of the two main columns was the artillery—two little three-pounders in the first, two six-pounders in the second.

Nathanael, riding in the rear, gazed up at the cloudless sky. It was going to be brutally hot. The army had marched about four miles, he judged. Still there was no alarm. His hopes for a complete surprise soared.

Then, from up ahead, came a scattering of shots. Moments later, a horseman came careering back: "Colonel Lee reports a body of the enemy approaching, sir!"

Nathanael put spurs to his horse. Coming up with Lee's advance, he found them deployed in the woods across both sides of the road, meeting a headlong charge by a force of British cavalry, followed by red-coated infantry.

When Colonel Stewart learned of the Americans' approach, he decided it was probably only a scouting detachment. He sent Major John Coffin out with 150 infantry and 50 cavalry to investigate. It was this force which Lee had met.

Coffin thought the American advance was militia who would run the moment they saw the enemy. His cavalry charged them at full speed, and found themselves in a hornets' nest. From behind trees and bushes the men of

Sumter's corps picked them off coolly, rider after rider. The rest of the British horsemen fled. Then Lee's infantry charged the enemy foot soldiers with the bayonet, while his cavalry galloped to their rear. The redcoats scattered in all directions, throwing away their muskets.

Nathanael rode on in front of his first column. Lee moved swiftly ahead with the advance force. He soon met a British advance, sent forward hurriedly while Stewart got his main army in battle formation. Then, as Lee moved his infantry out to the flanks with the cavalry, Nathanael ordered the first main column ahead to deploy and fill in the gap in the center.

Then all swept forward as the three-pounders began to belch and roar. The enemy line was driven back. And now, as they fled, Nathanael could see the rest of the British army drawn up.

Stewart had put almost all of his men in a single long line. It extended from the steep banks of Eutaw Creek across the road and up to a ravine at its left end. On both right and left were British Regulars. Nathanael recognized the troops in the center as Colonel Cruger's Tory defenders of Ninety-Six. On the far right of the British line were the remnants of Major Coffin's cavalry. The enemy had two six-pounder cannon.

Behind the British formation, Nathanael could see their tents, still pitched, in the clearing around the brick mansion. For an instant his thoughts flashed back with misgivings to the battle of Germantown. There had been a sturdy house there too—the stone dwelling of the Tory, Benjamin Chew. The Americans had had the British on the run there until some of the redcoats poured down a murderous fire from its upper windows. Would the balls of his light cannon bound harmlessly off Eutaw House, as they had from the one in Germantown?

There was no time to worry about it now. The battle had begun in a deafening roar and crash of artillery and musket fire. From his post behind the first line, Nathanael wanted to fling his hat in the air and shout, "Huzza!" The militia there were holding their ground, returning the British fire. He knew Stewart would not dare order a bayonet charge against such a stone wall of defense.

Many men were falling on both sides, but neither yielded an inch for some time. At last, however, the British Regulars' superior experience and training prevailed. After firing 17 volleys, the American militia were forced slowly back.

Nathanael was determined to hold his best troops in reserve as long as possible. He wheeled his mount and shouted to Brigadier General Jethro Sumner, commanding the inexperienced North Carolina Continentals: "Bring your troops up!"

They too met Nathanael's best hopes of them. They stood like rocks and met the hail of British bullets with an even hotter fire. Stewart was forced to bring up his small reserve force to bolster the line. Nathanael saw it was time to throw the rest of his Continentals into the fight. He ordered the second line forward.

Opening their ranks, the militiamen of the retiring first line let the Continentals through. "Charge!" cried Nathanael, and rode forward with them. They rolled ahead like an ocean comber whose breaking crest was the bright steel of their bayonets.

The red-coated line wavered before the impact of the attack. It crumpled, and the enemy began to run. "After them!" Nathanael shouted.

He galloped forward, exulting. The battle was won. At last, it seemed, he had gained a complete victory.

Not yet, however. Gazing to the left, he saw the British there were falling back slowly, in good order. They were crack troops, light infantry and grenadiers under Major John Marjoribanks. Behind them, like some ill-starred hoodoo, stood the brick house.

Nathanael saw a furious welter of struggling men before its door. The Americans, using their bayonets like spears, were trying to drive the enemy from it; the British to get inside and close it.

Nathanael groaned as he saw a file of redcoats batter their way inside the door. There was another fierce struggle while they tried to close it, but at last it swung shut.

Then, off to the right, Nathanael saw a worse catastrophe. A bellow of rage welled up in his throat. "Those fools!" he muttered. "Are they daft?"

Instead of continuing after the routed British army, many of the Americans were foraging among the tents of Stewart's camp for food and other booty, sure that the battle was over.

A storm of lead began to whistle down on them from the upper windows of Eutaw House. Nathanael ordered the artillery up to bombard it, then galloped forward to get the men among the tents back in ranks. Suddenly his horse collapsed under him, killed by an enemy bullet.

There was no time to obtain another mount. As Nathanael stumbled ahead on foot, Marjoribanks' troops and the remainder of Major Coffin's cavalry charged down on the British camp ground. Some of the American cavalry tried to halt them, but were repulsed with heavy losses.

The soldiers in the camp fled before the British onslaught. Then the enemy seized the American cannon; as Nathanael had feared, they had proved useless against the brick walls of Eutaw House, and the fire from inside had killed or wounded all the artillerymen.

Nevertheless, most of Nathanael's army was intact and in no disorder. A new mount having been brought up for him, he rode back and rallied them. They reformed their line, ready to go on fighting. The enemy too was back in ranks.

Should he renew the battle? Looking at the tired, sweat-stained faces of his men, he saw that the merciless sun might strike down as many as the enemy's bullets. And it took no more than a glance at the heaps of scarlet-clad dead and wounded strewn over the whole battlefield to tell him that the enemy had suffered frightful casualties. He had accomplished his purpose. Stewart's army was seriously weakened.

He ordered a retreat. As the army fell back toward its camp, the thirsty men flung themselves down at the edge of a stagnant pond by the wayside to gulp down its muddy water.

The British made no attempt to pursue. They were content to make the best of a hollow victory. Stewart had lost nearly 40 per cent of his army—about 500 killed and wounded, with 400 taken prisoners. The American casualties were severe—about 500 in all—but not disastrous.

Nathanael Greene had now fought four major battles. By military standards he had lost them all, yet the objectives he had achieved were as great as if he had won them all. After the battle of Eutaw Springs, Lieutenant Frederick Mackenzie wrote in the journal he kept of his experiences in the Revolution: "The more he is beaten, the farther he advances. . . ."

Stewart's crippled army limped toward Charleston. Except for that area, the British had lost all of North and South Carolina.

Now Lord Cornwallis was about to reap a bitter harvest which he had sown in his long pursuit of Nathanael's army through North Carolina.

*. . . that burying ground which you had chosen.* SIR HENRY CLINTON

Now the results of Nathanael Greene's masterly retreat through North Carolina and the battle of Guilford Courthouse were having their tremendous and far-reaching impact upon the entire Revolution. When Lord Cornwallis retired with his battered army to Wilmington, North Carolina, he walked into a trap which Nathanael had baited. It was a trap from which he would only escape into a far deadlier one at Yorktown.

Cornwallis was furious when he learned of Nathanael's march into South Carolina, for he was helpless to do anything about it. Not only was Lord Rawdon's army at Camden, 150 miles distant, but three large rivers lay in the way. Cornwallis knew all too well what would happen if Nathanael caught his weakened British army between two of them.

His only other means of aiding Rawdon would be to wait for transports to carry his army by sea to Charleston, whence he could march for Camden with greater safety. This was what Light Horse Harry Lee had believed would happen. But that would take too long; the Americans would already have struck at the British posts in the interior of South Carolina.

Cornwallis decided to march north into Virginia. He thought this might lure the Americans into following him and thus giving up their campaign in South Carolina. In

Virginia his army would reinforce another British one which was trying to seize control of that state.

On April 24, 1781, the day before the battle of Hobkirk's Hill, Cornwallis's army of 1435 men marched toward Virginia. Nathanael was not foolish enough to follow him. Besides, Lafayette was already in Virginia with about 3000 men.

Cornwallis's army arrived at Petersburg on May 20. In that city he met and took over command of the force there under the traitor Benedict Arnold, who had become a British brigadier general. Cornwallis now had about 6000 troops.

At this time, Washington sent Anthony Wayne with 1000 men to reinforce Lafayette. The Americans then moved toward Cornwallis, who fell back gradually until he reached Yorktown.

Yorktown stands on a long, narrow peninsula jutting into Chesapeake Bay between the James and York rivers. An army camped in such a place was in a strong position, but it would be difficult if not impossible to march out again if the way were blocked by an enemy.

That possibility did not worry Cornwallis. He was not in the habit of making such a mistake in tactics as to hole up an army where it could not escape. If it should be necessary to get out, his troops could leave by sea, since the British navy controlled the American coast. Nevertheless, Cornwallis had made a mistake far more serious than his ill-advised pursuit of Nathanael Greene's army in North Carolina.

Then there began a great chess game in which the richest prize in the history of the world was at stake—America. The opponents were General Washington and Lord Cornwallis. The pieces on the chessboard were the American armies of Washington and Lafayette, the French troops commanded by the Comte de Rochambeau, the British armies of Sir Henry Clinton and Cornwallis, the British fleets under Admirals Thomas Graves and Samuel Hood, and the French fleet commanded by Admiral François de Grasse.

Washington's army was on the Hudson River a little above New York. He was planning an attempt to recapture the city from Clinton. Rochambeau was with his French army at Newport, Rhode Island, which the British had abandoned in 1779. He was in favor of a campaign in Virginia.

Washington changed his mind about assaulting New York when he received startling news in August. The big French fleet which had been operating against Admiral Hood's British fleet in the West Indies had sailed for Chesapeake Bay.

That altered everything. With powerful French warships patrolling the sea off Yorktown, Cornwallis might be trapped. Washington decided to strike there.

He was a master at this kind of strategy and tactics. The most important thing was to keep Sir Henry Clinton ignorant of his moves, for Clinton had between 15,000 and 17,000 British and Hessian troops at New York. If he found out what was afoot he would surely send a mighty force to Cornwallis's aid.

Washington's strategy was to make Clinton think an attack on New York was about to begin. He concentrated his army along the shore of the Kill van Kull, the waterway separating New Jersey from Staten Island, as though the assault on New York would come from that direction. Nearby, he had large supply depots established, and along the shore he collected a great flotilla of boats.

Then, on August 25, the combined American and French armies stole away and marched south with all speed. It was a week before Clinton found out what had happened, too late to give chase.

By the time the allied armies reached Chester, Pennsylvania, Washington had word that the French fleet was at the mouth of Chesapeake Bay. Now he had only one worry. He learned that Admiral Hood's fleet from the West Indies had arrived at New York, where that of Admiral Graves lay. The combined fleets had then put to sea, looking for the French.

When Admiral de Grasse heard of it, he too put to sea. Off the entrance to Chesapeake Bay, the two armadas met. In the battle, the French frigates and monster ships-of-the-line battered the enemy warships so badly that they had to sail back to New York for repairs.

Then, just as had happened at Newport, catastrophe suddenly threatened the Americans' hopes. De Grasse informed Washington that he was going to sail for New York and fight the British fleet again.

This time, however, there was no General Sullivan to affront the French admiral. Washington and Rochambeau prevailed upon De Grasse to stay.

Now the French fleet controlled the sea off Yorktown. The trap had been sprung, and Cornwallis was caught fast in it.

The American and French armies laid siege to Yorktown. Cornwallis had thrown up strong defenses, and the disadvantage of being on a peninsula became an advantage, since it could only be approached from one direction by an army on land.

The allied armies dug parallels that brought them closer and closer to the fortifications. They mounted cannon which hurled shells into the beleaguered town. The destruction they wrought was fearful.

For nearly three weeks, Yorktown held out. Then, on

October 19, 1781, Cornwallis too surrendered what Sir Henry Clinton sourly described later in a letter to Cornwallis as "that burying ground which you had chosen."

The Americans had won the Revolution. Nathanael Greene was not there to see the great victory, but he had laid the foundation for it in the pine barrens, swamps, and red-earth country of North Carolina. Yorktown would not have happened save for his retreat.

# 15 ★ ★ ★ ★ ★ ★ ★ ★ ★ ★ ★ ★ ★ ★ ★ ★ ★ ★

*Here is my journey's end.*
WILLIAM SHAKESPEARE

After the battle of Eutaw Springs, the American army returned to the High Hills of the Santee to rest and recuperate from that bloodiest engagement of the Revolution. There, when the news of Cornwallis's surrender at Yorktown was received, a great celebration was held. The troops paraded and the cannon thundered salutes to the crushing victory.

The war was over, and yet it was not over. It would be nearly two years before the final treaty of peace was signed in Paris. Nathanael did not believe the British were ready to give up, and he made preparations for more fighting in the South. His aim was to drive the last of the enemy from South Carolina by capturing Charleston.

With Yorktown won, he expected to obtain large reinforcements from Washington's army. But Sir Henry Clinton's powerful force was still in New York. Washington too believed there would be more fighting, and did not wish to weaken his army. He did send detachments under Anthony Wayne and Arthur St. Clair, but the Southern Army's strength was still only about half of British General Leslie's at Charleston.

Nathanael moved the army to a camp outside that city, but he was not strong enough to assault it. Leslie did not try to drive the Americans off, however. For a year there was a stalemate, with the two armies jabbing at each other in skirmishes.

For Nathanael it was a year of constantly mounting difficulties. Indeed, one of these tribulations almost ruined him financially, and afflicted him with a sea of troubles for the rest of his life, and his family for years after his death.

For a time all went well in the camp. It was in one of the most fertile regions of America. Vast plantations furnished the army all the rice it could eat, as well as vegetables, fruit, and poultry. Foraging parties shot game in the swamps and forests of live oaks draped with Spanish moss. Until summer came, the weather was balmy and delightful.

At first Nathanael was happy too, though he fidgeted over the enforced delay in moving against Charleston. From everywhere came gratifying praise of his accomplishments.

His old friend Henry Knox wrote to John Adams, who was in Holland as American Minister: "Without an army, without Means, without anything he has performed Wonders." Adams, who as a member of Congress had often bitterly criticized Nathanael's actions, wrote to John Jay, the American Minister to Spain, that the battle of Eutaw Springs was "quite as glorious for the American arms as the capture of Cornwallis."

Congress, which voted Nathanael a gold medal, was about to appoint a Minister of War. Although four other generals—Henry Knox, Philip Schuyler, John Sullivan, and William Heath—were being considered, the members agreed that no better man than Nathanael could be found. But he refused the post, as he would do later when another was offered him. He was thinking only of being at home with his family when the war ended, and to make up for the years of companionship that had been lost to him and to them.

The states in which Nathanael had been fighting showed their gratitude handsomely. North Carolina gave him 25,000 acres of land. South Carolina presented him with a large rice plantation known as the Boone Barony, on the Edisto River. Not to be outdone, Georgia gave him one of its richest rice plantations, Mulberry Grove, on the Savannah River.

All these tributes were pleasing, but the happiest event of that spring of 1782 took place April 5. On that day a light, four-wheeled carriage drawn by two fast-stepping horses rolled into the American camp.

It had made the long journey from Philadelphia, driven by Nathanael's aide, Robert Burnet, who had gone there to plead with Congress for reinforcements. But it was not to greet Major Burnet that Nathanael burst out of his headquarters with a joyful shout and ran toward the vehicle. Burnet had a passenger—Kitty.

No sooner had she heard of Cornwallis's surrender than she was on her way, heedless of the arduous journey and approaching winter. One of Nathanael's former aides, Major William Blodget, had escorted her as far as Philadelphia. There, heavy snow and bitter weather had marooned her until February.

Nathanael had not seen his beloved wife for nearly three years. By the time she arrived, his troubles had begun, but they were all forgotten in the glad reunion.

There was much to talk about. Kitty had left six-year-old George Washington Greene with friends in Philadelphia to be educated. The other children were with relatives in Rhode Island. There were plans for the future to be discussed.

A round of social activities began, for Nathanael had

made many friends in the Charleston region. One of these affairs nearly put an end to his command of the Southern Army.

General Leslie was an agreeable fellow, but Nathanael was his enemy. When he heard how the Greenes were being entertained, he hatched a plot which would put a very fine feather in his cap if it succeeded. He too had many friends in the region. He persuaded one of them, a lady of a distinguished family who lived outside Charleston, to invite the Greenes to dinner.

Kitty was delighted. The foxy General Leslie was delighted too. He was so pleased with himself that he seems to have forgotten that ladies will gossip and to have bragged indiscreetly about what he was going to do. Some friends of the Greenes in Charleston heard of it.

Nathanael and Kitty arrived at their hostess's magnificent plantation on the Ashley River. While they were meeting and talking with other guests before dinner, a messenger from Charleston clattered up, asked to speak to Nathanael, and whispered a few words in his ear.

The Greenes did not stay for dinner. The haste in which they departed was downright discourteous, but they got away before the house was surrounded by dragoons Leslie had sent to capture the commander of the Southern Continental Army.

This bit of trouble was as nothing to those which now beset Nathanael. The blazing, steamy heat of the summer sun in South Carolina and the stagnant water in the vast swamps around Charleston bred disease. Hundreds in the camp fell ill of malaria and dysentery, and in five months 200 soldiers died.

Although Nathanael moved the army to higher, drier ground, fever continued to ravage the camp. He remained well, but several of his officers fell ill, and Kitty showed signs of doing so. General Leslie gave permission for them all to go in safety to an island off Charleston. There they gradually recovered in the bracing sea air.

The soldiers had other troubles. Their clothing was ragged, and once again there was a shortage of food, especially meat. South Carolina had allowed Nathanael to seize what provisions were needed, but the farmers of the region complained so bitterly that the permission was rescinded.

One of the principal suppliers of the army was John Banks & Company in Virginia. For a time John Banks, head of the firm, was able to buy clothing and provisions on credit, but as usual the government in Philadelphia had little money to pay the bills. At last Banks's credit was exhausted. He came to Nathanael.

"Unless you will sign my notes, guaranteeing payment for supplies, I can obtain no more, General," he announced.

Banks seemed to be an honest man, and the army's lack of clothing and meat was desperate. "Very well," Nathanael agreed, "I will sign the notes." He was going to regret it the rest of his days.

It was not only their nakedness and hunger that made the soldiers restless. Some had not been paid for two years. And peace negotiations between America and Britain had begun. The men did not understand why they could not go home.

"Some of our men are trying to get those from Maryland to join them in a mutiny," Lieutenant Colonel Josiah Harmar of the Pennsylvania troops reported.

"Who are their leaders?" Nathanael asked.

"I don't know," was the reply, "but it is common talk in the camp."

"You must watch and try to obtain proof of it," said Nathanael.

Harmar's vigilance was soon rewarded. Conclusive evidence was found that a Pennsylvania sergeant had openly proposed to the men that they deliver their officers up to the British. Nathanael had the whole army drawn up to see the sergeant hanged. There was no more talk of mutiny.

At last, in October, British transports sailed into Charleston harbor. General Leslie had received orders to abandon the city.

He was to take with him all Tories of the region who wanted to escape the vengeance which otherwise would surely fall upon them once the last of the British troops in South Carolina were gone. There was an agonizing wait while they were rounded up. Then, on the morning of December 14, 1782, after the Tories and thousands of their slaves had boarded ships destined for Florida, where they would make new homes, the British regiments embarked. Close behind them the triumphant American army marched in and took possession of Charleston.

Things were better for the soldiers after that, but they were still impatient to leave. Not until April, however, did news come that preliminary peace terms had been signed in Paris. Now the men could go home.

Nathanael had to stay until all had left, but Kitty was worried about the children and anxious to get home to Rhode Island. She sailed for Philadelphia in one of the first transports to leave. From there she went northward overland, stopping off at Princeton to get George Washington Greene, who had been tutored by Dr. John Witherspoon, head of the college there.

It was midsummer before the last of the troops left

Charleston. On August 11, 1783, Nathanael departed in a carriage with two of his aides. Colonel Carrington went along as far as Richmond.

It was a long, slow journey. Everywhere crowds gathered to cheer Nathanael. There were bonfires in the streets, cannon salutes, receptions, dinners, and speeches. Governors, other public officials, and friends greeted him. In Baltimore he was welcomed by his old battlefield companion, Otho Williams. Philadelphia gave him a tumultuous reception. Then, at Trenton, he had a joyful reunion with the man he idolized and respected above all others. It had been three years since he had parted with General Washington and set out on his way south.

From Trenton, Nathanael returned to Philadelphia on business. Here a jolt of bad news confronted him. John Banks had used the loans he had obtained for supplies to engage in some risky speculations. They had failed, and he had gone bankrupt. Nathanael found himself responsible for payment of the notes he had signed for Banks, but since he believed Banks had property which would take care of the debt, he did not worry too much about it.

Resuming his journey, Nathanael took passage at New York in a ship bound for Newport. His heart must have overflowed with joy as the vessel approached the dock there, for it was black with a vast crowd of shouting, cheering people.

He was home at last. Now he must think of the future, so different from what he had known in the eight long years of war. He decided he would remain in bustling Newport for a while, and rented a fine old mansion in the city.

Kitty, who was expecting another baby, was not well, and for the time being the children, except for George, were left with the relatives who had been caring for them.

164

Soon afterward the Greenes' third daughter, Louisa Catherine, was born.

With his brother Jacob and cousin Griffin, Nathanael decided to operate ships in the trade to Charleston and other coastal ports. He also planned to raise rice on the plantations in the South.

He was famous now. A constant throng of visitors came to the house in Newport, not only old Rhode Island friends and relatives, but many of his former officers and soldiers. Lafayette came. So did Kosciusko and other notables.

Nathanael's troubles were far from over. He was being hounded by John Banks's creditors for payment of the notes he had signed. At last he journeyed to Virginia, only to find that Banks had recently died, almost penniless.

He was facing ruin now. The investments he had made with some of his brothers in privateering during the war, as well as other ventures, had not been very successful. Neither did the new trading company prosper. In 1784 a hurricane destroyed half the rice crop on his South Carolina plantation.

There seemed one hopeful break in the dark clouds of his misfortunes. He had bought valuable timber land on Cumberland Island, off the coast of Georgia. He decided to begin logging operations, only to find that over 200 former Loyalists were looting the land of its timber. He appealed for help to the state of Georgia, and the thieves were chased away; nevertheless, without money to finance the logging, he could accomplish little.

Reluctantly, Nathanael asked Congress to aid him in his desperate financial straits. He hoped a grateful nation might grant him some compensation for his sacrifices in giving up his prosperous business in Rhode Island to fight for liberty. As usual, the wheels of government turned slowly. Congress finally did pay off the debt with which Banks had left him, but it was not settled until after Nathanael's death.

Now a blow of a different kind fell. While he was on a trip to the South, Nathanael received a challenge to fight a duel with one of his former officers, Captain James Gunn, whom he had once officially reprimanded. Gunn had nursed his grudge ever since; now he demanded satisfaction.

In the eighteenth century it was considered a disgrace for a gentleman to refuse a challenge without a proper reason. Nathanael did refuse because he felt a general could not be accountable to every man he offended during a war. Washington commended him in a letter in which he said, "Your honor and reputation will stand perfectly acquitted for the non-acceptance of this challenge."

Then Gunn wrote Nathanael, warning that he would attack him when they met. "He will not find me without a pistol in my pocket," said Nathanael. Nothing more was heard from the disgruntled man.

Now Nathanael came to a decision: he would move to Mulberry Grove, since it was important that he be near his southern plantations. It would not be easy to leave Rhode Island, where he had grown up and where so many good and old friends and relatives were. Yet he had come to love the South too. No blizzards howled there and no piercing cold took its icy grip in winter. The people were inclined to take things more easily and enjoy themselves. Perhaps New Englanders accomplished things faster, but the southern way of life was very pleasant.

There was great excitement and a bustle of preparation in the Greene household. All the family was together now. Of the five children, George was nine, Martha eight, Cornelia seven, Nathanael Ray five, and little Louisa not yet two. It was a happy time, though there was sadness too, for Kitty's sixth baby had died that summer soon after it was born.

It was the fall of 1785 when the family sailed for Georgia. Only Nathanael had seen Mulberry Grove before, and the others were enchanted when it came into view after their fourteen-mile journey up the river from Savannah.

It was considered the most beautiful plantation on the Savannah River. The house, built in the dignified Georgian style of the reigns of England's three Georges, stood among great oaks with their long gray garlands of Spanish moss. It was two stories high, with chimneys at each end for fireplaces to be used on chilly days in winter. Around it were a number of outbuildings, including stables, a coach house, poultry house, and an outside kitchen, common in the South in colonial days.

Beyond the house stretched the plantation's 2000 acres. Besides the rice fields there was land on which Nathanael planned to raise corn and other vegetables, and orchards with apple, pear, peach, apricot, plum, nectarine, pomegranate and fig trees.

Nathanael Greene had much to look forward to. He was in the prime of life, only forty-three years old. His years of command had given him an impressive air of authority. At first glance he seemed the picture of health. Although he was inclined to stoutness now, his frame was still muscular and broad-shouldered, his complexion ruddy, his eyes brilliant. Yet he was tired; the years of hardship and the worry over his financial troubles had etched lines on his face.

Nevertheless, Nathanael faced the future confidently. He was starting anew, a relatively poor man. It was not going to be easy to make a new success as a plantation owner, especially with the dark shadow of heavy debts hanging over him. But he had overcome far greater obstacles.

Now his children had a real father rather than an indistinct figure whom they knew only from what their mother told them. They would be much occupied in learning, for the Greenes had brought a tutor with them to oversee the children's education. But there would be plenty of time for Nathanael to romp with them, take them on his knee and tell them stories, and explore with them the wonders of the great plantation.

For his own relaxation, Nathanael had his cherished library. As for social pleasures, the Greenes entertained a host of friends and were entertained by them. Nathanael's old companion in arms, Anthony Wayne, had a plantation a few miles below Mulberry Grove. One of his faithful aides, Captain Nathaniel Pendleton, was a lawyer in Savannah. And he corresponded constantly with others. From France, Lafayette wrote, suggesting that George be sent to him to complete his education there, and the Greenes were seriously considering it.

The winter of 1785–86 passed, and spring came. One day in June, Nathanael decided to go down to Savannah on business. He took Kitty with him, and they stayed overnight with the Pendletons.

The next day, June 13, was very hot. The southern sun beat down brutally. By the time the Greenes reached William Gibbons's plantation, just below Mulberry Grove, the horses were exhausted, and they stopped there for dinner.

Before they resumed their journey, Nathanael went out bareheaded to look at his host's rice fields. Then he and

Kitty drove on to Mulberry Grove. Nathanael was feeling the heat and went to bed with a headache.

The next day he still had the headache, and remained in bed. The following morning it was worse, and there was a swelling over his eyes. That day Captain Pendleton arrived from Savannah. One look at Nathanael alarmed him so that he sent for a doctor.

In the eighteenth century, one universal remedy for almost any ailment was to bleed the patient. The doctor, not suspecting that Nathanael had suffered a sunstroke, drew some blood and went on his way.

The next morning Nathanael's whole head was swollen and inflamed. Another doctor was called. He drew more blood and applied blisters to reduce the swelling.

For two more days Nathanael lay in a stupor. All through Sunday, June 18, Anthony Wayne sat by his bedside. Outside the house, neighbors gathered, weeping silently.

Toward dawn on Monday, General Wayne called the family to Nathanael's bedside. His breathing was very faint now.

At about six that morning of June 19, 1786, it stopped.

They buried him in Savannah. To the slow music of a dirge and muffled drumbeats, regiments marched in the funeral procession to the cemetery while minute guns in the fort thundered a last salute. Today Nathanael rests in honored glory beneath a monument in the center of Savannah.

During the Revolution, while Nathanael was on one of his visits to Philadelphia, an artist painted his portrait in his general's uniform. It was presented to Congress to be hung on the walls of its meeting place.

One may look at the picture and find, as some people

did when they saw Nathanael Greene himself during the Revolution, a resemblance in that noble, resolute face to his idol, George Washington.

Both were great generals. Both were notable for determination, resourcefulness, and integrity. And both achieved great triumphs. Nathanael Greene's greatest one was his retreat to victory.

# Bibliography

ADAMS, CHARLES FRANCIS. "The Battle of Long Island," *American Historical Review*, I (1895).

AMORY, THOMAS C. *The Military Services and Public Life of Major General John Sullivan.* Boston: Wiggin & Lunt, 1868.

————. *The Siege of Newport.* No publisher given, c. 1900.

BASS, ROBERT D. *Swamp Fox.* New York: Henry Holt & Co., 1959.

BILLIAS, GEORGE ATHAN. *George Washington's Generals.* New York: William Morrow & Co., 1964.

BLYTHE, LE GETTE, and BROCKMANN, CHARLES RAVEN. *Hornets' Nest—the Story of Charlotte and Mecklenburg County.* Charlotte: McNally & Loftin, Publishers, 1961.

BOLTON, REGINALD PELHAM. *The Defence and Reduction of Mt. Washington.* New York: Empire State Society, Sons of the American Revolution, 1902.

BOWEN, CATHERINE DRINKER. *John Adams and the American Revolution.* Boston: Little, Brown & Co., 1950.

BOYD, THOMAS. *Light-horse Harry Lee.* New York: Charles Scribner's Sons, 1931.

BOYNTON, EDWARD C. *History of West Point.* New York: D. Van Nostrand, 1863.

BRIDENBAUGH, CARL and JESSICA. *Rebels and Gentlemen—Philadelphia in the Age of Franklin.* New York: Oxford University Press, 1962.

CALDWELL, CHARLES. *Memoirs of the Life and Campaigns of the Hon. Nathanael Greene.* Philadelphia: Robert Desilver, 1819.

COWELL, BENJAMIN. *Spirit of '76 in Rhode Island*. Boston: A. J. Wright, 1850.

DAVIS, BURKE. *The Cowpens-Guilford Courthouse Campaign*. Philadelphia: J. B. Lippincott Co., 1962.

DE LANCEY, EDWARD F. "The Capture of Mt. Washington." Paper read before the New York Historical Society, 1876.

DE PEYSTER, J. WATTS. "The Battle of Eutaw Springs," *The United Service* (September 1881).

DRAKE, FRANCIS S. *Life and Correspondence of Henry Knox*. Boston: Samuel G. Drake, 1873.

DRAKE, SAMUEL ADAMS. *Historic Mansions and Highways Around Boston*. Boston: Little, Brown & Co., 1899.

———. *Old Landmarks and Historic Personages of Boston*. Boston: James R. Osgood & Co., 1875.

DUPUY, R. ERNEST and TREVOR N. *The Compact History of the Revolutionary War*. New York: Hawthorn Books, 1963.

FULLER, OLIVER PAYSON. *The History of Warwick, Rhode Island*. Providence: Angell, Burlingame & Co., 1825.

GARDEN, ALEXANDER. *Anecdotes of the American Revolution*. Charleston, S.C.: A. E. Miller, 1828.

GRAYDON, ALEXANDER. *Memoirs of His Own Time*. Philadelphia: Lindsay & Blakiston, 1846.

GREENE, FRANCIS VINTON. *General Greene*. New York: D. Appleton & Co., 1879.

GREENE, GEORGE WASHINGTON. *Life of Nathanael Greene*. New York: Hurd & Houghton, 1871.

GREENE, NATHANAEL. "Nathanael Greene's Letters to 'Friend Sammy' Ward," *Rhode Island History*, XV (1956); XVI (1957); XVII (1958); XVIII (1959).

GREGORIE, ANNE KING. *Thomas Sumter*. Columbia, S.C.: R. L. Bryan & Co., 1931.

HALL, EDWARD HAGAMANN. *Fort Washington and Its Related Fortifications*. New York: Empire State Society, Sons of the American Revolution, 1902.

HARASZTI, ZOLTAN. "Besieging Boston with a Dwindling Army," *Bulletin of the Boston Public Library*, VII (May, 1932).

———. "The Last Stages of the Siege of Boston," *Bulletin of the Boston Public Library*, VII (September, 1932).

HUDLESTON, F. J. *Gentleman Johnny Burgoyne*. Garden City: Garden City Publishing Co., 1927.

JOHNSON, WILLIAM. *Sketches of the Life and Correspondence of Nathanael Greene*. Charleston, S.C.: Printed for the author, 1832.

LEE, HENRY. "Letter to Nathanael Greene, Aug. 17, 1781," *Siege of Yorktown Papers*, II, 10, Pierpont Morgan Library, New York.

LEFFERTS, CHARLES M. *Uniforms of the American, British, French and German Armies in the War of the American Revolution*. New York: Printed for the New York Historical Society, 1926.

LIPPITT, CHARLES WALTER. *The Battle of Rhode Island*. Newport: Mercury Publishing Co., 1915.

LOSSING, BENSON J. *The American Revolution and the War of 1812*. New York: New York Book Concern, 1875.

*National Portrait Gallery of Distinguished Americans, with Biographical Sketches*. Philadelphia: Rice, Rutter & Co., 1867.

PATTERSON, SAMUEL WHITE. *Horatio Gates, Defender of American Liberties*. New York: Columbia University Press, 1941.

SCHARF, THOMAS, and WESTCOTT, THOMPSON. *History of Philadelphia*. Philadelphia: L. N. Everts & Co., 1884.

SHERMAN, ANDREW M. *Historic Morristown, New Jersey*. Morristown: Howard Publishing Co., 1905.

SIMMS, W. GILMORE (ed.). *The Life of Nathanael Greene*. New York: George F. Cooledge & Bros., 1849.

SINGLETON, ESTHER. *Social New York Under the Georges*. New York: D. Appleton & Co., 1902.

STONE, FREDERICK D. "The Struggle for the Delaware," in *Narrative and Critical History of America*, Vol. VI. Boston: Houghton Mifflin Co., 1887.

STRYKER, WILLIAM S. *The Battles of Trenton and Princeton*. Boston: Houghton Mifflin Co., 1898.

THAYER, THEODORE. *Nathanael Greene, Strategist of the Revolution*. New York: Twayne Publishers, 1960.

TOMPKINS, DANIEL AUGUSTUS. *History of Mecklenburg County*

*and the City of Charlotte.* Charlotte: Observer Printing House, 1903.

Treacy, M. F. *Prelude to Yorktown—the Southern Campaign of Nathanael Greene.* Chapel Hill: University of North Carolina Press, 1963.

Trevelyan, George Otto. *The American Revolution.* New York: Longmans, Green & Co., 1899.

Valentine, David N. *History of the City of New York.* New York: G. P. Putnam & Co., 1853.

Waring, Alice Noble. *The Fighting Elder, Andrew Pickens.* Columbia, S.C.: University of South Carolina Press, 1962.

Washington, George, and Greene, Nathanael. "Washington-Greene Correspondence," *New England Magazine,* New Series, XV and XVI (September 1901–August 1902).

Watson, John F. *Annals of New York.* Philadelphia: Henry F. Anners, 1846.

Winsor, Justin (ed.). *The Memorial History of Boston.* Boston: James R. Osgood & Co., 1881.

# *Clifford Lindsey Alderman*

is the author of *Stormy Knight: The Life of Sir William Phips,* a Junior Literary Guild selection, which brought to thousands of readers a new picture of life in Colonial America; and *The Privateersmen,* the story of those men who fought the enemy ships during the Revolution and the War of 1812. Both books are Chilton publications.

A native of Springfield, Massachusetts, Mr. Alderman graduated from the United States Naval Academy in Annapolis and later took his graduate studies in chemical engineering at Massachusetts Institute of Technology.

During World War II he returned to the naval service, after a career in editorial and public relations work, and emerged as a commander in 1945 at the war's end.

Mr. Alderman's many books on history, American and European, have made him a favorite of readers everywhere. His three adult novels, all based on American history, are *The Arch of Stars, To Fame Unknown,* and *The Silver Keys.*

For young people he has written *The Vengeance of Abel Wright; Joseph Brant, Chief of the Six Nations; Samuel Adams, Son of Liberty; Wooden Ships and Iron Men,* and a book about the Bill of Rights and Runnymede, *That Men Shall Be Free.*

$4.50

# Retreat to Victory

## The Life of
## Nathanael Greene

### by CLIFFORD LINDSEY ALDERMAN

There is little doubt that Nathanael Greene was second only to George Washington as the greatest American general of the Revolution. He was gifted in countless ways and surmounted the many obstacles he encountered to gain those goals he sought after most. These obstacles which beset him from boyhood on only helped mold the character of an indomitable American.

Greene, born in Rhode Island in 1742, had a hunger and a passion for knowledge and he was persuasive enough to convince his Quaker father that he should have higher education and spend what money he earned on books.

At the outbreak of the Revolution a regiment was organized in Rhode Island and he marched to join the Colonials at the head of the Rhode Island volunteers. When the officers were chosen, Nathanael in one jump advanced from private in the Kentish Guards to brigadier general in the new regiment.

His first opportunity to distinguish himself came after the British evacuation of Boston. He was in command on Long Island, but before the battle there had begun, he was stricken with a fever. When the British routed the Americans he was tossing on his sick bed.